Nanna

Best Wishes

Heather Coupland

DON'T
CRY
NANNA

By

Heather Coupland

Edited by Jill Morris

Illustrated by Dez Wilson

CENTRAL PUBLISHING SERVICES
West Yorkshire

ISBN 1 903970 48 2

Published
by

Central Publishing Services
Royd Street Offices
Milnsbridge
Huddersfield
West Yorkshire
HD3 4QY

www.centralpublishing.co.uk

Acknowledgements

My niece Jill Morris for her huge input, her tireless work with various stages of the manuscript, all the fun we had while re-drafting, and for unjumbling what I thought was unjumblable.

I would also like to thank the following people without whose additional help, I would never have completed this book.

My friend Carole, whose early help and encouragement kept me going.

Dez Wilson, for doing a brilliant job of recreating my story in pictures.

My brothers Graham and Arnold (Jon) for filling in the blanks.

My husband Robert, daughter Michelle and son Matthew for their constant support, and for not tiptoeing out every time I read bits to them.

Pennine Tearoom in Marsden, for not kicking us out after spending hours rewriting, with only cups of coffee.

Kevin Jones, for filling in more blanks.

The Colne Valley local history group's publication 'Exploring Old Marsden', the Huddersfield Examiner and the Huddersfield Canal Society, for research purposes.

Elizabeth and Terry for their positive comments on the first reading of the manuscript.

Edward, for bamboozling me with business banter.

MIDDLE OF MARSDEN
1950S

KEY

1 - JUNCTION P.H.
2 - UNCLE HAROLDS
3 - TUNNEL END
4 - PAROCHIAL HALL
5 - CO-OP
6 - RUSSELLS TOYSHOP
7 - FRANK MANLES
8 - MOORHOUSES
9 - POST OFFICE
10 - MECHANICS HALL
11 - INFANT SCHOOL
12 - CO-OP SHOESHOP
13 - NELLIE BEARDSALLS
14 - TWO DUTCHMEN P.H.
15 - JOHNSONS
16 - ADULT SCHOOL
17 - COVER PHOTO TAKEN ON THIS BRIDGE
18 - PICTURES

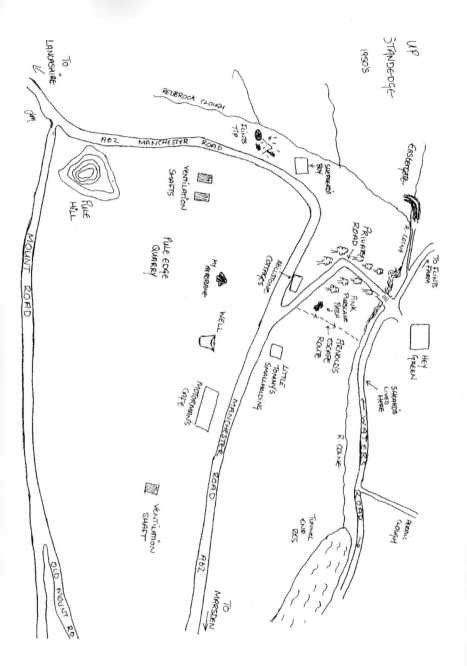

For my 4 grandchildren
Jordan, Jaydee, Samuel and Nia,
whom I love dearly.

FOREWORD

Isn't it strange how certain sounds, smells and objects trigger off memories, whether we like it or not. In this case, the object is a small child's coat, similar to the one worn by a very young Princess Anne; tailored at the waist, then falling in gentle pleats around a full skirt. The style may be the same, but the little coat hanging in Heather Coupland's wardrobe was not made of expensive material, and did not belong to the privileged child of a wealthy family. For this little brick-red coat is shabby, and always was. One button is missing, and another is blue, taken off a summer frock and stitched on with white thread. The buttonholes have been repaired, and above the cuff on the right sleeve is a crude darn.

The memories from this little coat go back to twelve months or so after the Coronation of Queen Elizabeth II, when Heather was a four year old, the youngest of four children living in poverty with their elderly Grandmother a mile outside a West Yorkshire village.

Against the backdrop of wild moorland and even wilder weather, Heather, with her passion for fantasy and horses, struggles, despite many problems, to keep her family together. A struggle which eventually becomes a fight for her freedom.

Heather Coupland has re-created the 1950's in a remote Pennine village, with the diversity of characters she encounters, the complexities of her relationships with them, together with the hardships endured by her family – all observed with a sprinkling of the wonderment which only a child can imagine.

Jill Morris

May 2001

Don't Cry Nanna

PART 1

CHAPTER ONE

SPRING 1954

A thin mist veiled the window, darkening the already dingy kitchen. It wasn't fit to play out so our Arnold said in his gruff little seven year old voice "Why don't we play at doctor's n' nurses? Ah'll be t'doctor cos ah'm eldest." Then turning to me carried on in his broad Yorkshire accent, "n' you can be t'patient, Heather, cos you're t'youngest." Our Kathleen, who didn't seem to mind what she was, ended up as the nurse. The stone flags on the floor felt cold and damp under my bare feet as I rooted around looking for bits of old rag that might come in as bandages. Our Kathleen, who had more sense than me, wore a brand new pair of red leather sandals.

Breezing around the kitchen with her cardigan sleeves rolled up to her elbows, was Nanna. Occasionally she would wipe two gnarled hands down the front of her pinny, then habitually nudge her tortoiseshell spectacles back onto her nose. Every now and then her long skirt would brush gently past us as she began clearing away the breakfast pots from the deal table which she had pushed to one end of the room to make more space.

"Whatever is this doin' 'ere, Arnold?" She pointed a bony finger at a battered old Dinky van which he had earlier manoeuvred around the sticky jam pot, but was now standing axle-deep in a packet of Silver Seal margarine, abandoned and forgotten in the excitement of our new game. Arnold dropped the length of band he was using as a stethoscope and went over to remove the offending toy. Then wiping its greasy wheels down the front of his grimy fairisle pullover he hurried back to his patient.

The kettle began to sing on the stove, softly at first, then with such force that clouds of hot steam began billowing from its spout. Nanna sped over to switch off the gas.

"Ah do wish you three wouldn't play on t'floor in this weather," she chuntered, pouring the hot water into an enamel basin, "you'll probably all catch yer deaths o' cold, then yer mother'll blame me."

Arnold

I didn't like the way in which she said 'mother', it made me feel uneasy. Mammy was a funny little woman who only visited once in a while, causing no end of bother when she did. As a rule though, Nanna seemed to put up with her ways, dealt with the havoc and cleared up the mess afterwards.

We had a father too, though we rarely saw him. He was divorced from Mammy, and lived in digs in the centre of Huddersfield. He was referred to by the family (even us children) as Wainwright, but known to them in the village as Charlie. The bit of brass he received from the dole office each week he spent on beer. Little or nothing went on food or clothing for himself or us. Nanna knew, as I did, that Arnold, Kathleen and me, and our older brother Graham who went out to work, were better living with her, than with either Mammy or Wainwright.

As the clatter of pots subsided, I heard Nanna pouring the dirty washing-up water out of the basin and into the slop bucket. Our cottage had neither a sink, a lavatory nor running water, so this saved us several journeys to the outside drain.

Then having whisked her mill shawl from the back of the couch, Nanna shook open two brown paper carrier bags and announced she was going 'stickin'. She paused in the doorway to add, "Ah'll only be gone a matter o' minutes, so don't do owt naughty while ah'm out." The door closed behind her. I shook off the strip of rag Kathleen was using to bandage my arm and shot off to the living room window, where I stood barefoot and on tiptoes, peeping around a dusty aspidistra.

The mist had turned to slanting rain through the grimy glass and smudged my view of the landscape, a brown eiderdown of windswept moorland and the busy main road which tore through the Pennines to Manchester. In the distance I could hear the buzz of traffic as it struggled up the hill, shattering the gloom with blurred cars and lorries.

Striding down the pavement, also blurred, was Nanna - her silver thread hair a glinting halo in the bad weather. One ungloved hand gripped the carriers while the other drew the shawl more closely around her. Like a cat watching a mouse I followed the lonely figure until she turned left, and disappeared down Private Road End. It had been windy, so Nanna would find lots of sticks down there for our fire. She couldn't afford a hundredweight of coal, so we relied on the sticks. I tried to imagine her, stooping down in the wet grass for a fistful of damp wood, then struggling up again and shuffling further down the lane. She might even get as far as the waterfall at the bottom, near the big house in the middle of the meadows.

Hoping Nanna would hurry up, I ran back to my brother and sister, who had set up surgery on the frayed square of coconut matting. They were chattering away like two little sparrows, unconcerned over Nanna's absence. Arnold, who always got very enthusiastic over everything he did, suggested we stage an accident - a road accident.

"Who wants t'be t'victim?" he asked, two big brown eyes flashing with malicious glee.

"I do. I do." Kathleen leapt to her feet.

Kathleen was very similar to me, and less than two years older. Soon, the blue cotton dress she was wearing would be passed down for me, and maybe her grey cardigan too, even though it was wearing at the elbows. Her short black hair, parted at the side, was fastened in a pink and white daisy slide. Like us, she was a pale matchstick, yet had a face round as a little ball.

"Reit, lie down then," ordered Arnold, smearing his runny nose on the back of his hand and dragging it dry down his shabby knee-length britches, "n' Heather'll cover yer up. There'll be summet there in that pile o' owd rags."

A musty smell filled the room as I rummaged around again looking for something else that would do. Eventually I came across an old sheet.

Kathleen had been sitting patiently on the bit of matting. When she saw the grimy sheet she came to life and rubbed her hands together, squealing "Give it 'ere 'eather, ah can do it, ah can cover meself up!"

I wanted to do it as well so together we tucked the grubby thing under the heels of her sandals then Kathleen launched herself backwards, whisked the rag over the top of her head and became a fatal accident.

After much prodding and poking, Kathleen was pronounced dead. Dead as a dinosaur. Dead as a squashed butterfly. We giggled over our many uses of that word. We were so taken up with our dead patient that Nanna had opened the door and walked in before we had even noticed. She was holding a soggy carrier bag bulging with sticks in each hand. Passing me the string handles, she panted, "Tek these over t'fireplace, Heather." Then adding, as I neared the cold hearth of the Yorkshire Range, "tip em out n' ah'll go n' fetch some more." She wiped her spattered glasses on her pinny, and shivered. Then, squinting across the dull room, she noticed our body.

The dash of pink on her cheeks painted by the morning's sticking vanished.

"What on earth are you three playing at!"

Nanna was very superstitious.

"Doctor's n' nurses," explained Arnold.

"An' Kathleen's been run over," I added innocently, bewildered by the sharp tone of her voice.

"Stop it! Stop it! Stop it!" Her voice rose to almost screaming, making poor Kathleen rise up from the dead. "Don't yer know yer can make things 'appen by doin' that?"

CHAPTER TWO

As the church bells chimed half past three on Thursday May 13th, Nanna ushered her little flock along the pavement in the middle of Marsden, towards Russell's Toy Shop. Nanna and I had walked the mile or so from our remote moorland cottage, down Manchester Road, and into the village. It was unusual to see Nanna in her grey worsted costume on a Thursday. It had been given to her by a friend and was usually kept for Fridays when it was pension day.

We'd met Arnold and Kathleen from school and Nanna had a few spare coppers in her purse. Perhaps Graham had given her a little extra. Or maybe the gasman had emptied the meter and left some change. Whatever the reason for her windfall, Nanna wanted to give us all a little treat.

The doorbell of Russell's Toy Shop tinkled softly and we trooped in. Mr. Russell was standing solid as his oak counter, littered with magazines, comics and newspapers. He smiled as we entered.

"Hello Mrs. Peace."

Nanna stretched out her arms like a mother hen and grouped Arnold, Kathleen and me in front of him. She didn't need to add "And don't touch anything."

Despite a layering of dust, the shop was aglow with every wonderful thing. It was like a picture from my Rupert The Bear* book of the cosily lit toyshop in Nutwood. Cheerful paint boxes, picture books, and a magnificant train set for Arnold, Dinky cars, showrooom-shiny, and rainbow marbles gleaming bright as our eyes. For Kathleen and me, the softest teddy bears with brown button eyes and velvet paws. Sitting in a row on another shelf were several blue-eyed dolls to choose from, each in a beautiful spotted frock and matching ribbon in its silky hair. But, more exciting than all of these, standing on the well-trodden floorboards in the far corner of the shop was a shiny red tricycle. It had large spoked wheels and a silver bell that twinkled like a little star in shafts of golden sunshine that slanted through the window. There was a boot at the back of it, and attached to the front, a wicker basket in which Nanna's bit of shopping could be carried home.

Kathleen and I might pedal through Market Place, Arnold up Towngate (the steepest bit) then the three of us could take it in turns to race along the pavement

---

* *Rupert the Bear annuals were my favourites, I bought them from jumble sales. Rupert lived in a beautiful cottage in a village called Nutwood with his parents. He roamed the countryside freely, had plenty of friends and lots adventures. Exciting things happened to him, which were made even more thrilling by Alfred Bestall's wonderful pictures, and the story briefly re-told in rhyming couplets underneath, which I preferred to the longer story.*

up Manchester Road.... But Nanna's modest budget didn't stretch quite as far as my imagination. Still, the thrupenny note books and black lead pencils, although not nearly as exciting, were enough to dance our sparrow legs home.

Nanna had even prepared something special for tea – a rice pudding, to which she had added a fistful of sultanas. We ate it outside, on the front steps, each with a bowl wobbling on the edge of our laps. On the top step Nanna left us three pots of warm, milky tea. There was no mistaking Kathleen's. It had been presented to her at school when Queen Elizabeth had been crowned, and stood like royalty among the chipped paupers. Nanna must have heard us slurping the last dregs for she breezed out from the back kitchen and stood in the doorway. Her best outfit had been replaced by her long navy skirt and flowered pinny.

"Why not draw a picture for me in your new books," she suggested, sweeping a glance at each of us with her soft, brown eyes. Our notebooks had been abandoned on the forth and fifth step the moment Nanna had announced the rice pudding was ready. We made a scramble for them.

With the dirty dishes clutched in both hands Nanna hung about for a while in the door 'oyle[*]; listening patiently to the running commentary delivered by each of us, as 'ouses, twees and gardens were scribbled onto blue lined sheets. Teatime traffic tore along the tarmac only yards from where we sat. Although Nanna's hearing wasn't too bad for someone who was 76, she still strained to hear our excited voices. This road, forever echoing the rumble of lorries, motor cars and the Oldham bus, was normal to us, like the sheep and shepherd that walked the hills.

I think it was these miles of open moorland which rolled further than my eyes could, swallowing up birds and finishing somewhere at the bottom of the sky that made Nanna move to Millstone Cottage in the first place.

"I didn't want no terraced 'ouse with a gloomy back-yard, did I 'eck," she'd once told me.

It must have been hard for Nanna to keep her eye on us all the time. While we were drawing we were being still so she turned and went indoors. But we were soon wanting to do something else and drifted away one by one. It was Nanna's rather large and balding besom brush lying on the stone flags that distracted me. As if it was a much-loved toy, I dragged it the length of the garden wall to where the bus stopped. There, not bothering about the wonky broom handle, I began to sweep the pavement clear of leaves. In no time at all I had umpteen heaps scattered along the tarmac. Meanwhile, Arnold and Kathleen had crossed the road and were kneeling on the grass verge opposite. They were poking around in a mountain of pebbles that had been left there by the roadmen. Passing vehicles smothered their voices but sometimes a tinkling laugh rang through the warm evening. They'd scratted up an old tin pan, which

---

[*] *Translate as doorhole. Doorway.*

they were gleefully trawling through the pebbles. For a while I stood fiddling with the broom handle, digging rotten wood out of it, watching them, left out but still not wanting to play. They were repeatedly filling their new toy to the brim with pebbles. Perhaps Kathleen had decided that, thrilling as it was, their saucepan lacked a spoon or something similar, because all of a sudden she sprinted across the road as though she was an Austin Healey. She tried to find a stick, which would do to stir with. Then, she grabbed one and I could only watch as my small dark-haired sister in her faded cotton frock and red sandals scampered back onto the road.

Nanna was scrubbing the top of the kitchen table when I ran in and clung straight away to her pinny. Within seconds there was a loud knock on the door which sent her scurrying off to see who was there. The man who stood there was holding himself up by leaning on the doorjamb so he wouldn't fall inside. He raised his head – his face was like one of our candles – and with what seemed an enormous amount of effort, he looked at us through bulbous, frightened eyes.

"Missis", he began in a faint voice. I crept nearer to Nanna and tried to hide among the sprigs of lavender around her apron. "I think I've... I think I've run over your little girl..."

Nanna was down the steps and across the road. I followed.

Our Kathleen, her pale cheeks stained with tears, was half sitting, half lying on the grass verge opposite. Arnold was standing beside her. Nanna dropped to the ground, cried "Oh Kathleen, Kathleen, what ever 'ave yer done? What ever 'ave yer done?" Kathleen, eyes brimming with tears, began to wimper.

Nanna quickly lifted up the hem of Kathleen's frock; I didn't know what she'd seen but she dropped it again. "Oh, no! No! Oh, no!" She cried. Gathering the little bundle gently up into her arms she wept, "Oh, Kathleen, Kathleen. Oh, Kathleen." Kneeling beside them, they were upset, so I was upset too. Above us, the bulky lorry sulked. Its wheels big and black and still.

Nanna was cradling Kathleen on her lap and talking quietly to her. "The ambulance is going to take you to 'ospitle," she whispered. The lorry driver had already flagged down a passing motorist and asked him to go to the Motorman's café and phone for an ambulance.

Kathleen, in a voice that was as weak as a pot of tea, asked, "Will ah cum 'ome, Nanna?" Nanna kissed her gently on the back of her head. "Yes love, yes love... one way or another... one way or another."

Nanna urged me to kiss my sister then.

"Arnold... Arnold... you cum 'ere as well - give Kathleen a kiss." Together Arnold and I crept closer to Kathleen. Her little elf face was white, her lips two bilberrys. Although I didn't like the look of her, I knew something was terribly wrong and that I must do as I was told. I think Arnold knew too, and he was crying.

Somewhere in the confusion two policemen arrived. After hurriedly gathering a few details one of them stood in the middle of the road and stopped the traffic in both directions. Then Doctor Hande came.

He took one look at Kathleen and asked Nanna if he could take her into the house. Very carefully he lifted my injured sister off Nanna's knee and carried her across the road and into the cottage. I trailed behind, looking at the traffic down Manchester Road, bumper to bumper like a long crocodile, with ridges of car-roof scales, it twisted past Mrs Medcalf's and the Motorman's Café.

Looking around for somewhere to lay Kathleen, Doctor Hande spotted the settee and laid her on that. Dashing into the kitchen he shouted, "Salt, salt – I need some salt." There was none of that in our cupboard and a moment later he darted out again. Pushing past the young policeman, standing at the door, he said, "I need some salt... some salt... to disinfect the wounds with." With that he ran down the steps and out of sight.

Kathleen lay still on the settee. Taking first one step and then another I walked, very slowly, towards her. Standing beside her I stared at her bloodstained frock, her pale face and unseeing eyes. Why didn't she sit up and giggle, like when we played doctors and nurses?

Outside I could hear lots of people chuntering all at once, but not Arnold's voice. I wanted him here in the room with us, so why wasn't he. I didn't know where he was.

A minute later Doctor Hande ran in, carrying a large drum of Sifta. He waved it under the nose of the young policeman as he hurried past. "I've got some from an elderly neighbour..." he said, "told her there had been a *slight* accident."

Then the ambulance arrived. So did Mammy. Joe Iredale, from next door, had driven down to Towngate to fetch her. He said our Graham was on his way.

"Don't blame Arnie," Kathleen whimpered as the ambulance men squeezed her through the door on a stretcher. I ran out of the house, and watched from the steps as my sister disappeared headfirst into the ambulance. The last thing I saw of her before the two big doors were slammed shut were the crepe soles of her red sandals.

The sudden clang of the bell made me jump, and people scattered like leaves across the causeway as the ambulance set off, flattening my forgotten roadside leaf piles as it went. Above it all I heard Nanna screaming, but I couldn't see her until some of the people had faded away. Then, there was Graham, bent over her. I moved away as he helped her up the steps and back inside. I followed them in.

Eventually Arnold returned. He had been taken to Mrs Woodward's, who, he said, amongst other things, had given him a lettuce and tomato sandwich for tea. Nanna cried when she saw him and pulled him close, weeping loudly as she buried her head into the crook of his neck. Then lifting me off the floor she sat me on her knee and continued to weep till it grew dark and Graham had to take a taper from a jar on the mantlepiece to light the gas mantle. Passing car headlamps splattered nasty lights on our walls. Drab, yellow ghostlights in horrible moving shapes, like squashed animals being peeled back and replaced by more squashed animals. I shivered in Nanna's lap and clutched tighter to her pinny

After thousands of animals had squashed round the walls, the door opened, Mammy slunk in. Graham jumped up out of the easy chair; Nanna looked at her expectantly.

"It's h'over." Mammy collapsed on to the old black horsehair couch. "It's h'over… there were nowt they cud do. She died two hours ago."

At eleven o'clock the following Tuesday Graham took Arnold and me to Mammy's, ready for the funeral. Nanna was too upset to go. Mammy was dressed darkly (and she had tidied the house).

First to come and show her respects was a lady who Mammy knew from years ago. Then a teacher from Marsden Infant School knocked on the door.

"I'd just like to say how very sorry we were to hear about Kathleen," she said. "It was very tragic. She was a lovely little girl and she will be sadly missed. We've had a collection… and in here…" she pushed an envelope into Mammy's hand, "is nineteen pounds and fifteen shillings. It should go some way towards paying for the funeral." Before leaving she wiped her eyes on a white cotton handkerchief and patted Mammy gently on the shoulder.

A little later, two people arrived; grim Mr Whitehead the undertaker, and the post woman who normally delivered letters to our house, but now came with a sackful of sympathy. Graham and his best friend Reynold Quarmby, lifted Kathleen's tiny brown coffin from the table and onto their shoulders. Slowly, they followed the undertaker out of the house and along the cobbles. Mammy walked behind. Arnold and I cowered in the doorway, watching the grim procession up Towngate, past Corden's shop and toward St Bartholemew's.

. DEZ WILSON -

Marsden Church

Back at home that evening, Graham calmly told us what had happened. There had been no hymn singing, he'd said. Nobody to play the organ or ring the bells because all that stuff cost money, and even with the unexpected collection from the school, there would still be a certain amount to pay. There'd be no headstone on her grave. All there would be to show for her short life was a patch of brown earth that was within yards of the road that had killed her.

❧❧

Two days later Arnold was asked to give evidence at the inquest, at the County Court, in Huddersfield. Mammy had to go with him. Half an hour before she arrived Nanna tidied him up a bit. She combed his hair, pulled his socks up and handed him over to Mammy looking a little bit smarter.

The following night details of the inquest were reported in both the Huddersfield Examiner and the Colne Valley Guardian. Graham read out the report from the Guardian.

"WAITED FOR LORRY TO PASS" –

AND WALKED UNDER ANOTHER

INQUEST ON MARSDEN
SIX YEAR OLD GIRL

"A seven-year old Marsden boy gave evidence at an inquest on his six-year old sister, Kathleen, Mary Wainwright, who was fatally injured when she was knocked down by a lorry on the Standedge side of Private Road, Marsden, last Thursday evening.

"He was Arnold Wainwright, the only witness of the accident, who after giving evidence was told by the Deputy Coroner (Mr,T.A.S. Drake) that he had "done very well indeed." Later, in his summing-up Mr. Drake commented on the – "very admirable" way in which Arnold had described the accident.

"A verdict of "Accidental death" was returned by the jury.

"Arnold told the Coroner that he and his sister lived with their grandmother at 1, Millstone Cottages, Marsden. At the time of the accident they were playing with some pebbles near Manchester Road. He was on one side of the road and his sister was on the other. She was going to cross the road to him, but he saw two lorries approaching – one coming up the road and one coming down – so he shouted to her to wait until there was nothing coming.

"She waited till the lorry coming down the road had got past her and then came out from behind it," said Arnold. "The driver of the lorry coming up couldn't see her and she went under it."

"Answering the Coroner, he said that Kathleen was walking across the road. The lorry that knocked her down was "going slow."

"Kathleen Haigh, of 2, Towngate said she was the divorced wife of Charles Frederick Wainwright, and had reverted to her maiden name. Her daughter had had good health, eyesight and hearing. The last time she saw her was at dinner time the same day.

"P.c. R. Morton, of the West Riding Constabulary stationed at Marsden, said he arrived at the scene of the accident to find the lorry which had been involved stationary on the nearside grass verge, facing uphill in the direction of Oldham. It was a six-ton lorry.

"He interviewed the driver, Kenneth Turpin, of 6, Lane Gate, Cheetham Fold Estate, Hyde, Cheshire, who made a statement in which he said that he was driving his vehicle in the direction of Oldham at about 6-45 p.m. when the accident occurred. He estimated his speed at between 20 about 25 m.p.h.

"As he passed the lorry coming down the hill a child ran out from behind it in front of his lorry. He swerved and braked, and pulled on to the grass verge.

"*When he got out of his cab he saw that the child who had run in front of his lorry was a girl. She was sat up on the grass verge and was crying.*

"*At the inquest Turpin elected not to give evidence.*

"*D. G. S. Hirst, who was on duty at Huddersfield Royal Infirmary, said the girl was in an extremely critical condition. She was suffering from the effects of internal hemorrhage and was very much shocked. She was taken straight to the operating theatre and given a blood transfusion before being operated upon. Her condition gradually worsened, however, and she died less than two hours after being admitted.*

"*The cause of death was given by Dr. R. A. Garson, assistant pathologist to the Halifax area, as shock following multiple and severe injuries and internal bleeding.*

"*Summarising the evidence, the Coroner said the driver's statement bore out what had been said - "and said so very admirably" – by the little boy. The boy had said very clearly that the driver of the other lorry could not see her, and that in fact seemed to be the truth.*

"*It seemed clear that what had happened was that the girl had waited until the lorry travelling downhill had passed and then attempted to cross the road, and had been hit by the other lorry.'*

The report was cut out and put inside a little blue toffee tin with roses on the lid, in the cupboard above the alcove. Almost the same could be said for Kathleen's coat, which went under Nanna's pillow the night my sister died.

CHAPTER THREE

FROM AUTUMN '54 – '55

Kathleen came quite often to play with Arnie and me that summer. We'd tear about downstairs on cold, unswept flags, banging into the rocker and the horsehair couch, riding the carved dining chairs like horses, but taking care not to knock against the huge mahogany sideboard for on top of that were Nanna's lustres. She'd bought them second-hand from Joe o' Joebs in Slaithwaite for fifteen shillings, and woe betide anyone who was careless with the tinkly glass droppers or so much as scratched one of the hand-painted flowers. It didn't matter so much with the old chipped enamel candlestick which stood ragged next to the lusters like a poor relation, with its small finger of wax, waiting for the gas to run out.

Nanna came in from the kitchen, and stood over yesterday's ashes in the cold grate.

"Stop talking s' silly. Kathleen 'asn't cum back an' never will."

She'd no sooner said that than there was a knock on the door. It was the landlady Mrs Newton from Berry Brow near Huddersfield. Her camel coat brushed against the jamb as she waddled in.

Nanna said "Ah 'aven't got yer 7/6d this month," so Mrs Newton took half a crown, and wrote it in her book. As she was leaving, she glanced back. "I were sorry to hear about your Kathleen," she wheezed, pushing her glasses up her nose, and was gone. Arnold and me ran to the front window to watch her drive away.

"That's an 'illman Minx," exclaimed Arnold.

Mammy began coming up more after Kathleen died. She had even got Arnold to cross roads again. But Mammy wouldn't have been Mammy if she hadn't done daft stuff, and Nanna had shaken her head in disbelief at the news that Mammy had married a Polish refugee with a face more rotten than old fruit, and the unpronounceable name of Piotr Topczewski.

Each time I'd had to go to the house they rented in the middle of Marsden, his eyes would be rolling about underneath his glasses. He'd order Mammy to "Pass me zat bottle of wine," and she'd spring up immediately. If he didn't ask her, he'd push past her so hard she'd nearly fall over. I kept clear of the path between him and any wine bottle.

Most of my time though, was spent nearer home, watching Nanna stare blank at walls, not seeming to hear Graham's offers of warm tea.

What she did hear though was Graham's gramophone. "Don't play that love," she shook her grey head. "Not so soon after Kathleen."

A long time went by, and Arnold and I played out, often till after dark, and sometimes we were gone all day, skipping out to school with empty stomachs first thing and coming back late, never seeming to notice our hunger.

Another thing I never bothered about was how I looked. I always swilled my hands and face in a bowl of cold water each morning, but that was about it. The rest of me, and my crumpled clothes, were as black as the fire back. One morning playtime, at school, a little girl said my dress was dirty. "And," she added, after taking another suck of milk through a wax straw, "it'll show up on t'school photograph."

Heather

"Tint mucky," I snapped trying to defend myself and my hideous white surge frock. It was miles too big and each corner of its gigantic collar stuck out like two chapel hat-pegs. Red buttons (there should have been four but the top one was missing) clotted like blood on an old bandage.

Don't Cry Nanna

"It is mucky, so mer." She pointed a fat finger to a big black splodge shaped like Australia, then waltzed off, in her smart grey skirt to join a group of friends gathering around the milk crate.

The photographs, when they eventually arrived, were five shillings each. Nanna could only just afford one. "Mi frock dun't look mucky does it Nanna?" The words of that girl still stung in my ears. It was one of Nanna's bit-better days and she was kneeling on a pegged rug, blackleading the fireplace. But she stopped what she was doing and held the black and white picture at arm's length. She studied it for a moment. "No it dun't look a bit dirty Heather – what ever made yer think it would?"

If Mammy found out what that girl had said, she would come marching into school shouting and swearing. So I said nothing and ran outside to play.

Arnold had arrived home before me and was struggling across the moor with a bucket of water. He must have caught th'up bus[*] while I had spent my tuppence ha'penny at the sweet shop and walked home. "Arnie," I yelled above the roar of traffic, "ah'm coming over t'meet yer."

Arnold looked up for a moment, then staggered on like drunken Topczewski as the weight of the water unbalanced him. The road was busy, so I practiced the kerb drill I'd been taught at school. It seemed ages before there was a gap in the traffic but as soon as it was clear I skipped across the tarmac to meet him. As I danced along the narrow path the smell of diesel mingled with the scent of heather. Black-faced sheep eyed me, and moved away, a worried dark brown-jacket bird hovered above.

Arnold looked puffed as I approached him. His shirtsleeves were rolled up and his pixie face was red. We both had permanent bruises where the galvanised bucket kept bashing our legs. "Yer gunner spill it Arnie!" I yelled as he plonked the bucket down on a tuft of grass. It was only half full anyway but by the look of his wet shoes it had probably begun it's journey much heavier. Arnold bent down and grabbed the handle just in time to save himself another long hike back to the spring. "Do yer know what ah'm gunner do tonight 'eather?" His autumn-leaf eyes twinkled with mischief and an impish grin crinkled the corners of his mouth "Ah'm gunner mek an 'en 'ut."

"An 'en 'ut!" I repeated. "What do you want an 'en 'ut for when yer 'avn't any 'ens?"

"Cos ah will 'ave on Saturday. Mr. Robinson's giving me three. Yer can 'elp me if yer want."

---

[*] *The up bus from Huddersfield to Oldham which came over the Standedge past our house after it had stopped in Marsden. We called the one returning from Oldham 'Down'ill bus'.*

Heather and Arnold outside Millstone Cottages

We both seized the bucket and lugged it in the blazing sunshine down the sheep track, stopping every now and then to pick clouds of fluffy, white cotton grass and spiky olive bull-rushes.

Nanna was sitting on the couch when we got back, reading a story in the 'Red Letter'. The rest of the house was a shambles but the old black range shone like patent leather.

"Ah've brought yer some flowers Nanna," I said, thrusting the cotton grass and limp rushes in front of her. A faint smile crept across her wrinkled face as she reached out to take them. Arnold didn't stop to talk but continued his journey through the room to the kitchen where I could hear the slap of cool, clear water as he tipped it into the big earthenware pot.

"Come an' sit at side o' me Heather," said Nanna "an' ah'll show yer 'ow t'plait rushes." Perhaps Nanna's bad days were over and from now on she might always be like this. "There now", she said, as her knobbly fingers wove three of the green strands into one long one. "Ah'll 'old this end and you can finish it off." Tibby, our splotched cat, who had turned up one cold day last winter when we'd had enough coal to light a fire, and had stayed, leapt onto the couch and was shooed off.

Don't Cry Nanna

The plait wasn't perfect but Nanna wound a piece of black cotton around the bottom to secure it. "Ah've got a norse wip now Nanna," I said, charging around and beating it against my leg, "ah'm gunner 'ave a norse o' me own wen I grow up, a yeller en called Trigger." Just like the one in the Roy Rogers book I'd bought from a jumble sale for tuppence. Arnold threw himself on the settee laughing his head off. "That's daft, 'ow you gunner afford a norse. Don't yer know they cost a lot o' money?"

"Ah'm gunner save up, s' there. Anyroad ah'd rather 'ave a norse ner three silly owd 'ens anyday."

"Reit ah'm not gunner let yer 'elp me fer that," snarled Arnold.

"Fer heavens sake stop fratchin[*]." said Nanna. "Go an' mek yerselves summet t'eat."

It wasn't often Arnold and I fell out and when we did it wasn't for long. "You put kettle on 'eather," he said, "an' ah'll butter t'bread."

Swarms of flies hummed around the kitchen, sometimes landing on the jam pot and struggling off with tiny greasy feet when Arnold swished at them with the knife and a cry of 'Gerroff'. A bluebottle, or was it a blowfly, I never knew one from the other, was trying to get out of the closed window. Buzz, thud, buzz thud. If it is a bluebottle, I wondered, while ladling some water out of the crock and into the kettle, it dun't look a bit like a bobby.

But Nanna, on the night of the accident had screamed, "Get yer 'ands off me yer bloody bluebottle," to a policeman who tried to calm her down when she went for the driver of the lorry. Perhaps she hadn't meant bluebottle as in fly at all, but blue bottle as in Milk of Magnesia. Arnold might know.

He was standing by the table with four wedges of 'Turog' in front of him and mountainous crumbs. On two of them he had spread a thin layer of bramble jelly and the brown bread showed through.

"Yer 'avn't put ner margarine on," I said.

"There in't none. There in't much jam either." (Graham was right when he said he'd seen more food on a mousetrap than in our kitchen.) He scraped the blade of the knife around the glass jar, at the same time shooing away another daring fly that was just about to land on his sandwich.

"Was that a blue-bottle?" I asked in almost a whisper. I didn't want Nanna to hear in case it upset her.

"No, it's a fly. So is that, so is that, that, and that." He pointed the sticky knife to dozens of blackberry like bodies that were swooping, diving and creeping across the tabletop.

"Wat's difference?"

---

[*] Arguing.

"I don't know, stop asking questions." Arnold took a man-sized bite out of one of the wedges. "An' don't forget to put some sugar in mi tea... if there is any," he added.

Yorkshire Range

The blue sugar bag was an open flytrap on the table, with a spoon sticking out of the top. "One for me, one for Arnold, one for Nanna," I sang while shoveling heap after heap into three stained pots. I did the same to the tea leaves and the water, (which in my enthusiasm I hadn't allowed to boil), I continued "A drop for me, a drop for Arnold, a drop for Nanna." The brew was rather messy. Arnold told me straightaway it looked like the slop bucket, but Nanna was kinder.

"It does look a bit strong love, and no, I don't suppose the tea leaves will sink, but never 'eed, Graham'll be 'ere before long so ah'll 'ave one wi' 'im."

Graham had been working over and didn't arrive home until quarter past six.

Arnold rushed out of the house to tell him about his poultry, but I was too taken up with my comic to bother. (Beryl the Peril had just sharpened her dad's ice skates.)

"We'll be able t' 'ave eggs fer us breakfast," I heard through the open door. Graham mumbled something about feeding them, and there was a scraping as he propped his pushbike up against the wall.

I glanced up as he strode in, shaking his head about the hens. His hair, blacker than the inside of Bankbottom chimney, didn't shake with his head, it was held in place by a dab of Brylcream. His eyes, too, demanded attention. They were very dark and shone like conkers. Had it not been for his eyes, his cleft lip may well have been more noticeable. He was eighteen now and as thin as a latt[*].

"'ello," said Nanna, half turning round to look at him as he came in.

Graham greeted her with his usual "Ow do." Then marching past her, he went into the kitchen. Trailing behind him, was Arnold.

"They're brown 'en's wi' a pink beak an ah'm gunner mek 'em a 'ut in t'garden."

Something about the tone of his voice told me that he wasn't quite getting the response that he had hoped for. Perhaps Graham was tired – if so we'd better watch out – he was inclined to get a bit grumpy when Arnold and I made too much noise.

"Will yer mek me a pot o' tea as well?" asked Nanna, raising her voice slightly in order to be heard above Arnold's.

As Beryl the Peril landed 'splosh' in a pool of icy water, I could hear Graham striking a match, and a whooshing as the gas ignited. Giggling to myself at Beryl's misfortune, I turned the page – to find – 'King Cussie' in a long red robe.

After making the tea Graham did exactly what we knew he would do, he lowered his lanky body into his favourite armchair; a deep, battered old thing that Mrs. Jones, the bank manager from down the road had given him. He switched on the wireless. There was a loud crackle and a whistle followed by a few more whistles and another crackle. Eventually he found what he was looking for – the Light Programme. Satisfied, he sat back and sipped his tea.

"The Archers," came a posh man's voice across the airwaves, "an everyday story of country folk." The Archers, which Graham said had started Whit Week five years earlier, when I was one, was on every weekday at quarter to seven.

"Sh!" He hissed at Arnold, who was doing summet noisy. "I'm trying to listen to this!" Dum, di dum di dum di dum, dum di dum di dum dum. As the tune faded away, the croaky voice of Walter Gabriel entered our living room. Arnold, without needing to be reminded again, knew that for the next fifteen minutes Graham would be totally absorbed in life at Ambridge, so it was no use

---

[*] *Fencepost.*

carrying on about them there 'en's. He slipped his stringy legs into top gear and raced outside into the sunshine.

Millstone Cottages had been built on the top of a row of damp underdwellings. As each tenant moved out, the house was condemned and therefore unoccupied. In one of these buildings, which we called the 'owd 'ouse, Graham kept a few rusty old tools and spent hours on end tinkering around with a clapped out motorbike. I knew that this was where Arnold was heading. After looking at the last picture of King Cussie, I closed the book and left it on the settee. From the garden I could hear a gentle tap, tap, tap. It was Arnold who had been into the 'owd 'ouse', and who'd taken, without asking, one of Graham's hammers. Graham would be very cross. I was just about to go down the steep steps to tell him so, when a black saloon car drew up on the grass verge opposite. The back door flew open and out stepped two brown fur-lined boots, as appropriate in this weather as an Eskimo in slippers. They were followed by two thin bare legs and the wonky hem of a spotty frock. The bird figure came strutting towards me.

"'eather!" Mammy squawked, so loud I was sure they could have heard her in Oldham. Despite a diamante hairgrip her raven hair was tangled and windswept. "Yer comin' back 'ome t'live wi' me an Piotr." Her hand grabbed mine and she began dragging me across the pavement. "We're gunner get yer a bed n' some new blankets."

"But Mammy," I protested, "Ah don't want t'live wi' you n' Topczewski, ah want t'stop 'ere wi' mi Nanna."

"You'll bloody well do as yer told!" she roared, dark eyes flashing.

"Let go," I pleaded. "Ah'll cum an' see yer, ah'll cum an' see yer every day if yer want me to."

By this time Arnold had run up the steps and was watching from a safe distance. Graham had rushed out of the house, Nanna rushed too, but slower. I think Mammy liked an audience, because as soon as she had one, her voice went even higher.

"If h'any on yer tries t'stop me tecking 'er, ah'll knife 'em!" she screamed. This wasn't as bad as it sounded. For one thing she didn't have a knife on her and for another she'd said it so often that, even for a six-year-old, it had lost it's impact.

"Wat the 'ell are yer lakin* at!?" snapped Graham. "Let go of 'er, yer 'erd wat she sed she dunt want t' live i' Marsden."

"An' what the blazes 'as it got t' do wi' you?" she bellowed back.

"Look, cum int' 'ouse an' 'ave a pot o' tea till yer've simmered down," he said.

---

* *Playing.*

Don't Cry Nanna

"Wat ever's up Kitty?" It was Nanna speaking now. She had finally reached us and was standing on the pavement in a flummox^{**}.

"Don't you bloody well call me Kitty," Kitty spat out poisonously, "Mi name's Kathleen. Do yer 'ear me. Kathleen!" With this she shoved me aside and clomped off across the road as quickly as she'd come. The taxi driver, who had been watching, spun the car round and sped off towards Marsden in a flurry of exhaust fumes.

Graham said she was a daft bugger and went off with Arnold to finish his 'en 'ut. I trailed indoors with Nanna. "Cum an' sit on me knee love," she said soothingly, "an' ah'll sing yer a song. When Miss Polly Oliver lay a sleeping in bed," she crooned, while I made myself as comfortable as possible on her bony knee, "A whimsical thought came into her head... "

It was a folk song from the First World War. I'd heard her sing it before.

"Sing it agen, Nanna." I begged.

"Ah'll teach yer a poem now," she said.

> "'When to the flowers so beautiful
> The Father gave a name,
> Back came a little blue-eyed one
> (All timidly it came);
> And standing at its Father's feet,
> And gazing in His face,
> It said in low and trembling tones,
> "Dear Lord, the name You gave to me,
> Alas! I have forgot."
> Then kindly looked the Father down,
> And said, 'Forget Me Not.'"

Arnold, with a bit of help from Graham, eventually finished his 'en 'ut', but the rotten planks that he had so carefully lugged up Manchester Road on his herry-cart[*], weren't proper shelter. Nor was the supply of corn, which he managed to cadge off Little Tommy, who owned the farm round the corner, enough to feed them. The thatched roof (sods from down the lane) leaked like a sieve, and it never occurred to Arnold to give the three scrawny pullets any water.

---

^{**} *In a state. Puzzled or embarrassed.*
[*] *Translates as Hurry Cart. A homemade wooden cart with wheels and some string to drag it with.*

CHAPTER FOUR

"Ah thought yer were s'posed to be visiting every day," said Mammy when I called after school the following Friday.

"Nanna an't been s'well, an' Arnie's 'ens died."

Mammy was wandering round the room, slarting* 'Wimsole' all over the carpet. It was *meant* to be diluted and used as a detergent.

"Where's Topczewski?" I whispered, still hanging in the doorway.

"Ugh 'im, 'e'll 'ave got paid t'day so 'es probably h'over at 'Two Dutch' getting drunk." She screwed the top back on the bottle as if it was Topczewski's neck she was wringing. Then banging it down on the stone sink said, "There's a jumble sale at 'Prockie 'all' tonight, do yer want t' cum wi' me?"

"Ah 'avn't got ner money." I'd been to Dixon's Sweet Shop again and spent my bus fare on a green lollipop, a stick of coltsfoot and two ha'penny black jacks.

"I 'ave," Mammy walked over to the sideboard. "Wainwright's sent me some maintenance money. Well, 'e knew ah wouldn't 'ave a-tolerated it much longer. Ah'd er summonsed 'im an' then 'e'd h'ave ended up in jail, an' 'e wouldn't 'ave liked that."

Surely the money should have been Nanna's, I thought, but I kept quiet.

"'ere, teck this," Mammy passed me a ten shilling note out of her brown leather purse. "Go an' get 'alf a pound o' boiled 'am fer t'tea."

I could have gone to Waterhouse's just across the road, but I knew if I went to Lunn's up Peel Street Mr Lunn would be sure to give me a piece of ham while I was waiting. He was an old man, was Mr Lunn, but not as old as Nanna. He had a jolly face and a gentle voice. I bet he was a nice dad too. Pasted to his window was a sign, which read:

JUMBLE SALE
MARSDEN PAROCHIAL HALL
FRIDAY 15th JUNE – 6pm
TEA & BISCUITS SERVED
ADMISSION 2d

If I got there in plenty of time I might find a Rupert book or a tennis ball.

I ran all the way back, swerving in and out of pedestrians like a dodgem car. Marsden was always busy on a Friday teatime. It was payday, so a lot of local

---

* *Sprinkling*

folk were out spending their hard-earned cash. Most of them worked in the Colne Valley's woollen mills. Bank bottom Mills at Fall Lane was probably the biggest, and employed several hundred people, including Graham. Within coughing distance, was Ottiwell's Terrace which had been built to commemorate the site of Ottiwell's Mill, whose owner, William Horsfall, the mill-owner, fell off his horse and died after being shot by Luddites in 1812. According to what my teacher said, he'd been afraid of the Luddites attacking his mill and smashing the shearing frames that were putting a lot of croppers out of work, so he'd defended it with a cannon. The Smithy of the two brothers, Enoch and James Taylor, who made the machinery, had one time stood on the same site as my school down Brougham Road. But to me the mills were just smelly, noisy places that made you sweat, and had smoky chimneys which poked up out of Marsden like the fingers of thin men pointing at clouds.

"Jumble sale starts at six, Mammy." I panted, slapping down the boiled ham and remaining change on the table. "Ah'll fill t'kettle." I only said this because I wanted to turn the tap on and watch the jet of water spurt out. And it was like magic when you pulled a chain and the lavatory flushed.

While I mullocked about, filling and refilling the kettle and wasting as much water as I liked, Mammy buttered bread. Considering that most areas of her life were in a complete mess, her house was quite neat and tidy. It had three rooms downstairs and a large, but cold kitchen with a concrete floor. On it stood an old gas stove and a tall cupboard where she kept tea, sugar and tins of Carnation milk. The living room, like the rest of the house, didn't have much furniture, but it was cosy and warm. Six mullioned windows gave a lovely view over the river Colne.

Mammy finished making the sandwiches, and with the Colne Valley Guardian spread out like a tablecloth, asked me to look and see if there were any feeders* wanted at the mill.

Apparently, at the end of her only week at school, Mammy had fainted, never gone back, and so had never learnt to read – except the odd words like TO LET, which went hand in wing with her butterfly lifestyle. So I had to drag myself away from the excitement of the sink, to help her.

"Feeders, fettlers and p... pe..." I struggled over a particularly hard word. "I can't read that Mammy it's too long."

"Never 'eed, miss it out an' go on t'next."

"Wan...ted for wo..."

"Woollen."

---

* *Feeders took raw material to make into yarn, by feeding it into a hopper, through a series of rollers into a scribbler. It came out like cotton wool and needed rubbing into soft thread before going off to the spinners who spun it into hard thread.*

"Woollen Mill," I continued, "Sl... Sla... Slack...cote Mills Delp."

"Delph. " Corrected Mammy. "That's ner good it's too far away. Is there owt else?"

"E...x...p..."

"H'experienced," chimed in Mammy again, probably wishing I could read much faster.

"Experienced men..."

"H'if they're wanting men that wint do either."

"No ah 'avn't finished yet Mammy – it sey's men...ders."

"H'o," she said, looking a bit puzzled. "Its still ner good, ah can't mend."

And so it went until I shoved the paper to the far end of the table and moaned "Ah'm fed up now."

"Ah well," said Mammy "ah'll just 'ave t' see if they'll set me on at Bruce's[*] again." She folded the paper and together we sat by the fireside eating our tea.

As soon as the church clock struck quarter to six, Mammy snapped up a shopping bag and off we went. It was only a two-minute walk to the Parochial Hall, but everyone tended to push and shove, so it was best to get there early. It was lucky we didn't pass anyone we knew because Mammy kept stopping to lift up her skirt. She was trying to tuck her laddered stockings into some white knicker elastic which she'd made into a garter. I went ahead slowly, pretending not to notice. Outside the hall, a short queue had already begun to form. Apart from three other children and a scruffy man in a brown trilby, there were mainly women.

"They should be h'opening doors soon" said Mammy, hopefully, rocking backwards and forwards. For the moment she'd forgotten about her garters.

Minutes later the shuffling of feet could be heard coming from somewhere inside the lobby, then the doors were flung open and we all piled in. Mammy chucked four pennies into an old enamel pie dish behind me. I hurried past clothes piled higher than Pule Hill and headed for the toys. Rummaging through battered boxes of jigsaws, building bricks, cars without wheels and a thousand other things, I found a rag doll with a green felt body and a violet dress. The fact that she didn't have a face was no bother – I could make one.

"'ow much is this please?" I asked a grey-haired lady in charge of the stall.

"A penny, love." I passed her the sticky sixpence my Mammy had given me. So now then, I had a doll without any features, two mouldy pennies and a thrupenny bit. Should I buy the game of Lotto, or look for a picture book instead.

By this time the hall was a flurry of activity. Octopus arms waved round stalls, picking and poking, lifting things up to examine them or shaking things to see if they worked. Somewhere amongst them was Mammy. It wasn't until I'd

---

[*] *A mill opposite my school on Brougham Road.*

managed to squeeze to the front of the book stall and buy Hansel and Gretal, a book about a rabbit going to a wedding and 'More Adventures of Rupert', that I saw her again. She was staggering towards me with her arms full of rags.

"See if this frock'll fit yer," she screeched above the racket. Although it was crimson velvet with a white lace collar, it was a bit shabby, and the hem dipped. I told Mammy it looked alright and stuffed it into a brown paper carrier bag.

After the jumble sale I had a choice of either walking home up Manchester Road or along the canal towpath as far as Tunnel End. I decided on the towpath. It had been a warm day and the sun still shone on the narrow strip of water. Like a troop of dancers enjoying the limelight, Pond Skaters skimmed along its surface. A stickleback, tempted by a tasty morsel, leaped into the air – dived – then disappeared into the murky water below. I didn't stop too long, I was eager to show off my new doll to Nanna and I scampered past brambles, hazel bushes, hogweed – tall as trees, purple-headed willowherb and creeping white clover. The smell of their perfume filled the air.

Tunnel End, Marsden

A train rattled across the railway bridge as I hurried below. At the exit of the tunnel I was half way home. On my right Tunnel End Cottages came into view. They had been built for the tunnel keeper to live in whose job was to keep his eye on the number of boats going in and out of the three-mile tunnel.

They'd started working on the tunnel in July 1794, I'd been taught, and it took seventeen years to finish it (There were that many problems, apparently, and I knew that tunnels, like horses, didn't come cheap). They joined the Huddersfield Narrow Canal to the Ashton Canal, which brought trade through the Colne Valley to Huddersfield – for a bit anyway, till trains whisked all the cotton, wool, coal and timber much faster. This left the path I was now walking along in a state of decay. The boats were long gone, so were the men and their families, leaving this pretty stretch of waterway to ducks, to moorhens and to me.

The stone steps, which would eventually lead me to Boat Lane, (so called because it was the route along which horses were led while the boatmen legged it through the tunnel, I'd found out) caused me to pant. Driven by excitement, though, I continued to run a little and skip a bit until, finally, I reached Manchester Road. Only a few yards, past Connie Medcalf's and the Motorman's Cafe, up our five steps and I was home. My excitement soon turned to disappointment. Graham was out, Arnold was nowhere to be seen and Nanna was fast asleep in bed. Not even Tibby was there to greet me; perhaps she was mousing down at Little Tommy's farm. Come to think of it, where was Tibby, no-one had seen her for days.

I was tempted to waken my Nanna – but I didn't. She hadn't been feeling well all week, so Graham had dragged her bed downstairs and put it in an alcove next to the fireplace. She laid with her back to me, her weary head resting on the mucky pillow. A scratchy woollen blanket and a man's ex-army coat covered her frail body.

Carefully, I lifted my new doll from the crumpled carrier bag, sat her in a corner of the sofa and went in search of a handkerchief. I remembered seeing one a few days before in the left-hand drawer of the sideboard – it was still there. It belonged to Graham, but he wasn't there to see me take it. Then, having found a pot to draw round, a pair of scissors and a blue biro, I set to work making a face. Before you could say 'Towngate' I had created the prettiest one ever seen. Well, it certainly looked pretty to me. The hardest part was finding a needle and thread and stitching it on.

We did have another doll in the house, but that had belonged to Kathleen. Nanna had wrapped it in my sister's Christening shawl and put it in a cardboard box underneath the window in the back bedroom. Although I knew, without ever being told, that it wasn't to play with – I did like to look at it. Sometimes I would sneak upstairs and peep into its cradle. It was laid as if fast asleep, with its eyes shut tight. It had come from Cousin Miriam's who was grown up now and had a confectioner's shop on Warehouse Hill. Because Kathleen's doll had lost most of its hair, Nanna had made it a blue flowered bonnet that fastened with a safety pin under its chin. If I was very careful, I could just about manage to unfold its shawl and peep underneath without disturbing it. It was dressed in a white cotton petticoat with a scalloped hem. On the top of that, but a little bit shorter, was an ivory pinafore, embroided at the bottom in a rich silver thread. Wrapped awkwardly around its right leg, to hide a small crack, was a grubby bandage.

"There now," I said, after a great deal of effort, "ah've done." With my own newborn baby lying across my knee I snipped through the strand of black cotton and inspected my handiwork. It didn't matter in the slightest that a row of great big galloping stitches were running round her face like the centre lines on Manchester Road. Nor was it any bother that her smile seemed lopsided, her navy nose looked broken, and one eye was higher than the other. She belonged to me, she felt soft to touch and I knew that I would cherish her forever.

"Ah'm gunner call yer Violet," I said proudly, and waited for Nanna to wake up.

❧

It had been six days since Tibby had gone missing and no one had seen her. I'd searched everywhere, calling her name and tch, tching. I'd been over the moor and down to the farm. Little Tommy said he hadn't seen her, but was sure that she'd turn up.

That same week Mr. Fitzgerald, the 'Cruelty Man', paid us a visit. He was short and stocky with a ginger mustache that wiggled when he spoke. He'd called

a couple of times before. I wasn't sure whether I liked him or not – but I think Arnold did. Perhaps it was his uniform that put me off. It was navy blue with N.S.P.C.C. written across his breast pocket for everyone to see. On his head he wore a peaked hat, a bit like a stationmaster and across his nose rested a pair of thick lensed brown rimmed glasses.

"Ave yer seen me cat?" I asked, the moment his head appeared through the door.

"Why hello Heather, what do yer say, have ah seen yer cat?" He repeated in his Scottish accent. I think he was surprised to see my Nanna in bed because he immediately went over to her. "And you Mrs. Peace" he said, "are yer not well?"

"Ave been feeling a bit dizzy, that's all" she waved her hand, as if it didn't matter.

Graham

With a voice filled with concern, he asked, "Are the children looking after yer?"

"Yes. 'eather's just made me a slice o' bread wi' lard on, 'aven't yer love?"

I nodded. "An' 'ave made 'er a pot o' tea as well, but we 'aven't got ner milk so she's 'ad it wi' out."

Mr. Fitzgerald said I was a good girl and patted my head. "And where's that rascal of a brother of yours?"

"Down Private Road wit lumberjacks. They're not lumberjacks really 'cos they 'aven't got checked shirts on. An' in my Roy Rogers Annual they all wear red an' black 'ns."

But our Arnold liked to think they were. He'd stand, fascinated, forgetting all about going to school, watching them chop dead trees down and drive off again in their truck. Some of the men gave him thrupenny bits for pulling the withered branches off, and he'd shoot off to Marsden to spend it on sweets.

"Lumberjacks." said Mr Fitzgerald, with a smile. "Well, well, well." He glanced around the room, asked Nanna if it was all right to sit down, then drew a dusty dining-chair nearer to her bed. I was rinsing a pair of dirty socks in a bowl of cold water. I'd stood the basin on an old wooden buffet that Nanna had had for donkey's years. The bar of pink Lifebuoy kept slipping through my fingers and skidded across the uneven flagstones, making me run barefoot, after it. When I caught it, it was covered in grit and felt like sandpaper. As I rubbed it backwards and forwards across the heel of my sock the horrid smell of carbolic filled the air.

Nanna and Mr. Fitzgerald were talking in hushed voices, but I had a good idea that what they were saying was something not so nice about Mammy. When I was wringing out my sock Mr. Fitzgerald stood up and walked towards me. "Heather" he said, as softly as his deep voice would allow. "Do yer think yer could leave yer Nanna and I alone for a while? There's something we need to discuss."

This sounded serious and I began to feel scared. But I did as I was asked. I dried my hands on a smelly towel, slipped on my plimsoles and followed him outside.

"Don't wander off because it won't take long," he reassured.

It was a cold, damp morning. A sharp wind bit the moor, the road, and the cars and lorries that cut through it. Normally I would have been romping around like a curious kitten, but today I felt more like an orphan. I was just about to have another look for Tibby when Mr. Fitzgerald came to the door and called me back in. As I made a start on scrubbing my other sock, Mr. Fitzgerald spoke to Nanna about a shop shut down in Town, and the price of milk.

That night though, I heard Nanna talking to Graham in the same low voice. The only words clear enough came like slaps - 'Teckin' em away.'

Two, maybe three days later, Tibby still hadn't turned up. Then, one breezy afternoon, I was playing on the causeway with a rubber ball when Louie Schofield came wobbling past. Her apple cheeks glowed. She lived at the Shepherd's Boy, a few hundred yards further up the road. Having got onto the habit of asking everyone I saw, if they'd seen Tibby, I began my little speech again.

"Wat's she look like, love?"

"She's all colours. 'er 'ed's same colour as 'er back – black an' ginger. An' she's loads o' white bits under 'er belly an' 'er chin."

"Well," she wheezed, "ah'm not sure, but ah think ah've seen one 'at looks a bit like that at bottom o' Warhurst's lane. But," she added, as I began running to where Warhurst's Lane joined Manchester Road, "It's been knocked down." I really believed, as I ran along the pavement and across the road, that Tibby would be exactly the same as when I last saw her. But what I actually found was nothing like. It was Tibby all right; I recognised her straight away. But instead of running to greet me with a friendly meow, she lay dead among the dirt and the pebbles. Her once soft, fluffy coat was matted with blood and her marigold eyes were closed. I was no crybaby, but as soon as I got home I flung myself on the settee with Violet, sobbing for Tibby, and sobbing for Kathleen.

Tibby

PART 2

CHAPTER FIVE

SPRING '56

In February, men arrived armed with picks and shovels, and began digging deep holes at the side of the road. Into the holes went tall, wooden telegraph poles, like limbless winter trees. Arnold and me went, coatless, to watch. Sometimes we sat on slimy green fallen stones, other times we stood, or leapt around shaking our arms and hands. It was hard to tell which of the streaming whitenesses were billowing from our mouths and noses, and which were the smelly cigarettes of the men.

"Why are yer doin' that?" Arnold asked them. "Wat's this for and 'ow long will it be before we can put a light on?"

The men laughed at Arnold with his knobbly knees and holey sweater, and often found him little jobs to do. One morning, after two of the men had dug deep into the earth at the top of Private Road, Arnold rushed through the drizzle into the house shouting at the top of his voice, "We've struck water, Nanna... We've got a well nearer t' 'ouse!" Believing we'd never have to cart water across the moor again we danced and whooped around the room. Nanna was lost for words.

Our celebrations were short lived. We later discovered the well that he had got so excited about was nothing more than top water which had seeped through the soil, forming a muddy puddle, and that we were destined to lug buckets full of water for ever.

Eventually, after all the spadework was finished, the electrician trudged in with his muck-caked boots, screwed in the bulb he'd brought with him into a fitting in the centre of the ceiling, flicked on the switch and hey presto. Arnold and I cheered, and tore around the house switching the lights on and off like a Belisha beacon.

"'ow am ah gunner pay t'bill?" was all Nanna could say.

For Arnold, this electricity stuff started sparking off all kinds of ideas. The three eggs, which LittleTommy had given him, just last week, were the exact things needed to construct his latest experiment. He built a tower out of books, bricks and boxes in the back bedroom and perched the eggs on top, about six inches beneath the light bulb.

"If ah leave em 'ere long enough," he told me, "they'll 'atch out."

But apart from wasting an awful lot of electricity (without Nanna knowing), little else happened. After weeks with not as much as a scratch appearing on the surface, Arnold had to admit defeat. But all his hard work had not been in vain. All that running up and down the dark staircase and black landing had given him a brain wave. What was needed here, he said, was an extra light – and who better to install it than himself.

Instead of going to school the following Monday morning, he spent his dinner money at Tom Chadwick's Hardware Store. Later he showed me what he'd bought. I craned over his cupped hands and saw strange bits and pieces, which Arnold cheerfully told me were twin flex, three-inch nails and an adapter. I followed him up the stairs, and watched as he screwed and fiddled with the stuff. "I'll have to connect this adapter to the light in t'kitchen, so shift yerself," he said, pushing past me. I didn't know how long he'd be so I just waited. He came back, beaming, grasping the kitchen light bulb and ran the flex up the staircase, hooking it over a nail on the landing. Finally he flicked the switch, and demonstrated how a pitch-black landing could look like a department store.

"Ooh Arnold, you are clever!"

"Yeah" he replied "Graham'll be reit impressed."

But later that evening, when Graham came home he took one look at Arnold's wonderful work and shrieked: "It's a wonder yer 'aven't electrocuted yer sen, yer silly little bugger."

And Nanna was right to be concerned about the paying the bill. After the second reminder, the power was cut off and we were back to burning candles.

❧ ❧

On April 21st, Arnold turned nine. Nanna had managed to scrape together one and sixpence ha'penny to buy him a quarter of Quality Street for his birthday. When he tipped them out of the bag to look at properly, it was like jewels cascading. I oohed and aahed over the shiny wrappers thinking they looked just like some pirates treasure Rupert had once discovered. Arnold's eyes were golden pennies as he scooped up his jewels, all six of them. I studied each one: one emerald shaped like a triangle; another emerald but longer, with two ends and a middle; a gleaming amethyst like an upturned boat, with squeaky twists of cellaphane at each end; a golden bar, again with twists, which might have made a rather funny long bow tie; a second amethyst, an oval one wrapped in shimmery foil; but the best one, not a jewel at all but a strawberry, ruby-red and heart shaped, flecked with yellow seeds and a green cellaphane stalk twisted up at one end.

If they were my spice* I'd have saved that one for last so I could look at it longer, but Arnold jabbed his finger at it and said "Ah'll 'ave that first" and had unwrapped it and shoved it in before another word came out. I managed to save the wrappers and put them in my scrapbook as a special addition to all the horses.

BACK ROW (FROM LEFT)
Michael Bray, Nicholas Kaye, Kevin Barrat, ...?..., John Warner, Stuart Davis, Colin Goldsborough, Anthony Watson, Kenneth Holroyd.

SECOND ROW FROM BACK (FROM LEFT)
...?..., Michael Wood, Margaret Cotton, Pat Blackburn, Lesley Davis, Lynn Wilkinson, Christine Robinson, June Crabtree, Sandra Rhodes, ...?..., Terry Wood.

SECOND ROW FROM BOTTOM (FROM LEFT)
Elizabeth Haigh, Jean Mosley, Susan Mellor, Pat Smith, Janet Chapburn, Pauline Hill, ...?..., Pam Dearnley, Heather Wainwright, ...?....

FRONT ROW (FROM LEFT)
...?..., Raymond Schofield, ..?..., Edward Lowe, John Dutton, Robert Powell, Kevin Carter, David Rowland.

---

* *Sweets.*

It wasn't too long after the few spice had settled in Arnold's stomach, probably forgotten by him but still glistening in my mind, that he got up early one morning with a beam on his grubby face longer than that gold bar with the twists.

"Ah've got a surprise fer yer," he grinned. "Ah'm gunner mek yer some breakfast, but yer've got t'stop in 'ere an' not look."

He disappeared into the kitchen and set up such a racket of clattering and chopping noises that it was an effort to stay sitting on the horsehair couch and not go peep.

By and by I smelt the smell of warm lard and wondered whatever he was making. It was taking too long to be a bit of lard on bread, and besides, he wouldn't have melted it. Then I heard a vicious sizzling and realised he'd got the tiny cast iron chip pan out from under the stairs. Last time I'd seen that, there were mouse feet tracking across the solid lard.

After a bit, Arnold came out with my chips on a plate, and a twinkle in his eyes. The last lot of chips I'd had were from Th'owd Stocks chip shop in Towngate, but by the time I'd got them home they were cold.

Cautiously, I stabbed a chip with the old black two-pronged fork, and put it in my mouth. I screwed up my face and almost choked.

"Wat they like?" Arnold laughed, dancing round the room. "Little Tommy gave me a turnip yesterday."

CHAPTER SIX

SEPT '56

It was near my seventh birthday, I wasn't excited, it would be the same as any other day. Our lándlady Mrs Newton turned up, carrying a paper bag. Again, Nanna was in arrears. Arnold happened to be around, and was zooming a wagon Mr Fitzgerald the Cruelty Man had brought him, up and down the couch back.

"Could you be quiet a minute, love," Mrs Newton asked. "I'm trying to talk to your Nanna."

Arnold went quiet but soon cheered up when he discovered Mrs Newton had left her bag for us. It was full of annuals. She brought some up sometimes. I put Violet down, and we pulled them out quickly in case they disappeared: Beanos, Dandys, Beezers.

"Great!" cried Arnold, even though I could probably read better than he could. It would have been nice to see a Rupert book, or Toby Twirl, or Fairy stories like what I got from jumble sales. But books were books, with words and pictures in. And I always liked arguing with Arnold over which Bash Street Kid was best. He grabbed a Beezer and flopped on the couch with it. I took a Beano to read to Nanna.

I'd never had a birthday card before, but the day after my seventh birthday I was excited to find a white envelope lying amongst the dust on the sideboard.

"Open it," smiled Nanna, "it's fer you."

I began tearing at the paper. Inside was a colourful card which opened up into a beautiful bunch of scented flowers. At the bottom, written in neat handwriting,

'From Mother'.

I knew that Mammy hadn't written it herself.

"Read it," said Nanna, proudly.

I read the verse out loud and concluded with the "From Mother."

"From Mother?" Nanna's eyebrows scrunched together. "What about my name - 'asn't she put my name on? Cum 'ere love, let me 'ave a look."

I walked over to the bed to show her.

"Well ah never! The cheeky beggar's only put er own name on. Ah' paid fer it an' all – ah gave 'er a shilling!"

Her eyes glistened with tears as she clipped a strand of white hair back into her tortoiseshell slide and rearranged her faded woollen shawl around thin shoulders.

"If this is what 'appens when yer get a birthday card," I thought, "I'd rather do wi' out."

When school started up again, my friend Christine asked me to come to her house at dinner time, but I still needed something to eat. Prowling around in Johnsons, looking for something to spend my five shillings on, I noticed Christine's blonde curls bubble up in different colours in the reflection of the big brass scales as she suggested a small tin of peeled tomatoes.

Christine lived up Dirker, the council estate on the northern hills of Marsden. I thoroughly enjoyed my walk there, peering at all the gardens along Dirker Drive and studying the coloured daisy petals of ice plants, and flowers which I had never seen before. I enjoyed my small tin of peeled tomatoes in her homely kitchen too, and continued to enjoy them for the next two weeks. By the end of the third week they didn't taste quite as good, and on the following Monday I decided I'd get more for my money by buying school dinner.

Ten days after my birthday, when I was going to Moorhouses* to buy in, it occurred to me I should pop into Towngate and at least thank Mammy for the card. Arnold had taken to sleeping there, so it would be nice to see him too.

"'e might walk 'ome wi' me," I thought while lugging my loaf, ½lb of Kraft margarine, packet of Typhoo and 2lb of potatoes past the Co-op and over the concrete bridge that spanned the River Colne. I opened the door to find Topczewski sitting at the table, smoking a cigarette.

I had always been wary of Topczewski, especially since the time he'd come up to my Nanna's and tried to strangle Graham. Fortunately Arnold and I had been out when it happened. Mammy had called for us early that morning, and out of the blue she had taken us into the village and bought us some food – iced buns,

---

* *A mixed business, which sold almost everything. The three sisters who owned it, Kathleen, Elanor and Eunice were all spinsters and I liked them a lot because they were always very helpful whenever I went in. It was one of the busiest shops in Marsden.*

boiled ham and a piece of polony. It had begun to snow quite heavily and soon the pavements had become like a wedding cake. As we'd trudged through cold streets, an acquaintance of Mammy's grabbed her by the arm and said, "'e ah've just seen your 'usband gettin' out of a taxi, Kitty, an' he 'ad blood pouring down 'is face." Brushing away a big fat snowflake that had settled on her nose, she'd continued, "'e said summet about yer mother 'ittin' 'im wi' a teapot."

"A teapot!" Mammy had yelled. "Wat the bloody 'ell's been goin' on?"

"Ah don't know," said the woman, "but if I were you ah'd keep well away, he looked fit t'kill t'me."

Mammy's face had turned as white as Connie Metcalf's steps. "Cum on you two," she'd said. "Let's get up that bloody road an' see wat's 'appened." She'd grabbed us by the hands and began to drag us up towards home. Making sure she avoided Towngate, she'd led us up Oliver Lane, down Garfield Place and over the bridge past the cobblers. As we'd struggled through the blizzard she'd kept going on about things I would have preferred not to hear.

"That bloody foreigner!" She'd shrieked, "Ah wouldn't ah put it past 'im t' 'av bloody well have killed h'our Graham. H'if 'es as much as touched a 'air on 'is bloody 'ed ah'll knife 'im... ah will... ah'll bloody well knife 'im! 'E were nowt but a bloody murderer during t'war. Ah can just see 'im now killing sumdi fer sake of it n' leavin' em dead in a pool er blood."

Why couldn't she have said, "Oh, don't worry, it'll be alright, it'll be summet an' nowt – you'll see." Instead her voice had risen even higher than the Mechanic's clock, which had frightened me even more. Arnold always knew the best things to say, "It'll be alright, Mammy, yer 'eard wat that woman said, me Nanna's clobbered the bloody swine. She probably did it before 'e could do owt t'our Graham. An' anyway, even if she hadn't, Graham wouldn't just stand there n' tek it. 'e'd er probably given as good as 'e got."

"Humph!" Mammy had hurried on. We'd trudged behind, watching the traffic slow to nearly walking speed. Somewhere near the Belgi Firm*, a car slid into a gutter.

"There's no point in waiting for th'up bus," Mammy had said "it'll never make it beyond Warrington Terrace." Hatless and gloveless, the three of us had battled our way along the pavement against the bitter east wind which blew cruel across the moor, swirling snowflakes frozen against our faces. It had whirled them around our heads and down the back of our legs. Arnold's nose and sticky-out ears had been as red as a pot jug in Mrs Beardsall's window; his face bluer than a bluebottle's.

A few other local folk, sensibly dressed in heavy overcoats and wellington boots, had struggled along the pavement towards Marsden. "'orrible weather," remarked one of them.

---

* *Local name for Belgian Mill – Bailey Ancion up Manchester Road.*

Don't Cry Nanna

Mammy had told us to put our hands into our pockets and walk next to the wall where it was more sheltered. This had helped a little bit – till the snow had got deeper and my secondhand shoes became sopping wet. Each step squelched and squished. Half of me had been desperate to get inside, but the other half reluctant as to what we might find there. Had Topczewski really killed Graham?

Eventually we'd reached home very cold and very, very wet. Arnold had run in front whilst Mammy pulled me along by my frozen hand.

"Bloody 'ell, look at this." Mammy had pointed to something *red* in the drifting snow. "That looks like blood t'me."

While we'd dried off in front of the fire, Nanna had told us everything.

Graham had pressed charges. But when the case finally went to court, Mammy had showed Graham up by arriving arm-in-arm with Topczewski.

The following night, Nanna had read out the report in the Huddersfield Examiner:

Aided by an interpreter, a Pole, Piotr Topczewski, of 2 Bridge End, Marsden, denied having threatened to kill his stepson, Charles Graham Wainwright, (18) of Private Road End, Marsden. Wainwright alleged at the Huddersfield West Riding Court on Tuesday that Topczewski had beaten and asaulted him at Private Road End on January 14th.

He said that Topczewski had married his mother about two years ago and that he had never been on good terms with him. He lived with his grandmother at Private Road End and on January 14th Topczewski called there. He was in a taxi and was looking for his wife with whom he had quarrelled the previous night. Wainwright said he refused to admit defendant and he thought that Topczewski had struck him so he hit him back. A fight followed and witness received bruises when defendant thrust him into a corner and hit him. His grandmother then hit Topczewski with a teapot, severely cutting his forehead. Wainwright said that his stepfather had then threatened to kill him if he saw him again, so he telephoned the police.

Topczewski gave no further evidence but said it was a family affair and that he did not want anything to be done about it.

The magistrates dismissed the case.

Now, there he was, an evil shadow in front of the orange glow in the grate.

"Where's mi Mammy n' Arnold?" I shuddered.

While I stood stock still in the middle of the floor, Topczewski sat himself down at the table again. He took one last drag of his Capstan Full Strength then twisted the tab-end into an ashtray.

"Let's find ze iron for your muzzer," he suddenly suggested. Before I knew it, his hand was in mine and he was leading me, shaking, into the other room.

Topczewski stood me next to the ceramic fireplace and ordered me to "stay zere!" He squared my shoulders with his nicotine stained fingertips, then slithered his wicked hands down my skinny arms. Satisfied that I was exactly where he wanted me, he crouched on the floor and peered up the chimney – shuffling first this way and that in order to see further. It was obvious to me that the iron wasn't up there, so what the heck was he doing?

After a furtive glance in my direction, he took one last look, then staggered to his feet. He led me upstairs, each splintered step creaking under us, into the back bedroom. The rank smell of old soot and damp wallpaper in the naked room peeled up my nostrils. Set into an inner wall was an old Victorian cast iron fireplace. With my hand once more gripped by one of Topczewski's, I was pulled towards it. The fall of our footsteps echoed loudly, there might have been a dozen of us.

"Wat's 'e keep lookin' up t'chimney for?" I wondered as he squatted on the floorboards ready to gaze into another opening. A few remaining cinders and a pile of ash were the only sign that the room might once have been slept in. He propped himself up again, tilted his head then gaped up the flue. He didn't speak, and I daren't, but once again he sized me up before resuming his ritual. I wanted to run, but he could probably catch me. Maybe if some soot tumbled down and got inside his glasses, I might just have time.

We had hardly got into the third room – *their* room - when footsteps pounded up the stairs. Suddenly, Mammy was flying across the room towards Topczewski, screaming like a mad crow and swearing. She grabbed him by the hair and yanked him towards the stair steps.

"Yer bloody h'article!" she shrieked as he tried to grab his hair back, stumbling backwards. I ran downstairs and listened to the fight, wondering what to do for the best. Then Topczewski came running down, followed by Mammy, still swearing and still swiping. Then Arnold burst in accompanied by two plain clothed policemen. (As soon as Mammy had seen *my* bag in the middle of the floor she must have sent Arnold rushing off to the police station.)

"May we sit down," asked one of them.

Mammy, who was still shouting words at Topczewski that I'd never heard before, turned to them and screamed, "'e bloody well wants lockin' up – do yer 'ear me? Bloody well lockin' up. An' if yer don't bloody well lock 'im up ah'll knife 'im ah will... ah'll bloody well knife 'im!"

"Now calm down, calm down Mrs...erm..."

"Haigh," snarled Mammy, assuming her maiden name, "Mi name's Haigh."

"Well Mrs Haigh, what seems to be the matter?"

"The matter," said Mammy, "is 'im! 'im." She pointed a witchy finger at my stepfather, who was sitting calmly at the table, a lop-sided smirk across his goblin lips. His eyes were as red as the tip of his cigarette.

For the next ten minutes it was bloody this and bastard that, till finally Mammy had spat out all the horrible curses she could think of, while I shrank into the chair, wishing I could disappear down the nearest mouse hole. Arnold was as quiet as I was. To the policemen's questions I simply said, "No," and spoke only when spoken to.

Finally the officer, who had been asking all the questions, stood up and said; "In view of the fact that Heather hasn't said anything that we can charge Mr Topczewski with, I'm afraid there is nothing we can do."

Mammy growled and when the policemen urged her to send for them should the need arise, Mammy growled again.

As soon as they had gone, Mammy opened the door, shoved my bag into my hand and pushed me out.

"Bloody well get back t'yer Nanna's n' don't cum 'ere agen," she yelled. "Wat the 'ell made yer cum in't first place ah don't know. Why don't yer use yer common sense yer stupid little bugger? Don't yer know 'e were gunner murder yer n' put yer up a chimley?"

CHAPTER SEVEN

WINTER '56-SPRING '57

After my lucky escape from the chimney at Towngate, we started having visits from Miss Newton, a prim welfare worker who made the effort to smile a lot. She hadn't seemed too bad till she started bringing Mr Bruce with her; a sharp, weaselly man, pricklier than a hedgehog, but not as nice. Unfortunately, Mammy was up the first day he came. She'd brought some Shirly* cakes with her. Her bird eyes met his, and she seemed to fathom him out straight away. After he'd gone, Mammy snorted, "Bloody welfare. Ah won't a-tolerate 'em. Ah wouldn't trust *him* wi' uncounted gold**!"

Autumn; crimson, blustery, faded away with the final lines of harvest hymns, and before long, it was carols we were singing. The Co-op windows, which had previously been stocked with bonfire toffee and Standard Fireworks, were now full of frosted cakes, sugar mice and cosy slippers. Even school was the most wonderful, magical place on earth. Chains of colourful paper looped from the ceiling, like in Rupert's house, and pictures of snowflakes were pinned to the wall. A nativity scene, which Miss Theaker had lifted carefully from a cardboard box, as she explained patiently the significance of each piece, had pride of place on a small rectangular table at the front of the classroom. In preparation for the school party we had all been busy making paper hats out of thin card and tissue paper. Mine, a fancy golden crown, was decorated around the bottom with cotton wool. I was looking forward to the party because last year there had been lemonade, iced buns, potted meat sandwiches, red jelly with custard and lots of fun.

Before that, though, there was the school pantomime and I had been chosen to play Rudolf. All I needed was a red dress. "The one you wore last week with giraffes on will do," said Miss Theaker. I would much rather have been a fairy but I supposed Miss Theaker thought there was as much chance of my Mother making me a glittering costume with sparkly wings as a trolley bus had of travelling from Marsden to Huddersfield without any electric. So a reindeer I was.

A few weeks later Miss Theaker said that on the night of the pantomime,

---

* Mammy's name for Chorley Cakes.
** Someone had once written a reference for Mammy, saying she could be trusted with uncounted gold.

she'd like us to invite all our parents to come and watch. Having understood her to mean that parents *must* attend, and although I would prefer Mammy not to be there, I thought I would have to ask her. I hadn't seen her for quite some time but there was no way I was going to knock on the door and risk being alone with The Goblin again. As it happened, Arnold, who was spending more time at Mammy's than he did at school, was watching out for me as I passed through the village on my way home.

"Cum 'ere, 'eather," he called. "Ah've summet t' show yer!"

"Wor is it?" I asked.

"It's a present me Mammy's bought me fer Christmas. Cum on 'urry up. Run!"

I belted along the flagstones behind him. His lanky legs increased in speed as he lengthened his stride. He was heading for Mammy's and as he skidded to a halt on the worn step I could see that the door was open and Mammy was there.

"Look, look!" yelled Arnold barging inside. Then grabbing the handlebars of a brand spanking new, red Raleigh bicycle, he continued "It's from 'arrops i' 'uddersfield. Me n' mi mammy went down on Mundi' n' they've delivered it t'day. Its pedals were back t'front," he spun one round, "'andlebars were upside down n' they were wrapped i' brown paper. An' look wat else she's bought me." He pointed to a Christmas tree about 3 feet tall, standing on the table beside him. I gazed in awe at the dozens of artificial branches that stuck out at angles from its skinny stem. Attached to the end of each shoot was a small cluster of scarlet berries. There was one in my Rupert book just like it.

"Can ah tek it 'ome wi' me?" I asked.

"No, it's mine!"

"It's t'stop 'ere," said Mammy, jumping to his defence.

"But I want one," I pleaded. "Ah've always wanted one, yer know I 'ave."

But Mammy knew so little about me, and even less about treating children equally! I hoped she'd say – "Well, seein' as ah've bought you a bike Arnold, Heather can 'ave t'tree." But she didn't.

Arnold was eager to show off his new toy and began to wheel it through the door. I was about to run after him when I suddenly remembered about the school play. But Mammy wasn't listening.

"Watch road, watch road!" she bawled after Arnold as he pedalled away. "Ah don't want yer getting knocked down!"

Arnold sped into the distance – his spindly legs working away like two little pistons. He wasn't paying attention either, but I expect having uttered the warning made Mammy feel better.

"Wat did yer just sey?" she asked after he'd gone.

"We're doin' a pantomime at Parochial Hall on Frydi – it starts at seven. Miss Theaker seys yer've t'cum n' watch. Ah'm gunner be a reindeer!"

"O… right… " She patted her Romany hair with a row of bony fingers. "Ah'll cum n' pick yer up from me mother's at six then."

She smiled as I left – a toothless smile that formed a gaping hole in her ageing face. It reminded me of the dark entrance to the Standedge Tunnel and for what must have been the thousandth time, I wished she would wear false teeth, grow a lot taller, talk a lot quieter and be more like Pat Smith's mum.

When I caught him up, Arnold was cycling to and fro between the Two Dutch and Corden's shop. Every now and then his silver bell shrilled in protest as he juddered over cobbles.

"Gi' er's a ride," I shouted.

"All right, but don't you dare fall off and scratch it," he said as he roller coastered towards me.

On the day of the play Nanna was propped up in bed when I arrived home from school. She asked me what I'd been up to.

"We've bin doin' about volcanoes," I replied, plucking up Violet and straightening her frayed dress, then glancing at the mountain of ash in the cold grate. The electric had been cut off again so we were back to burning candles. I reminded Nanna that Mammy was coming on th'up bus at six. Nanna straightened the shabby overcoat thrown carelessly over the thin blanket. On her bedside trolley stood an emergency soda siphon, half-full – if there was no one around to fetch her a drink. A packet of peppermints lay beside it.

"Ah'd better find mi red dress wi' giraffes on." I left Violet on the couch and darted into the kitchen and scratted through the rag pile. My dress was as creased as a scrunched up toffee paper and spotted with mildew.

"Rudolf the red nosed reindeer," I chirped whilst shoving my arms through the soiled sleeves. Soon I'd be on stage and it didn't really matter that Mammy would be there, Rudolf was probably a more important part than the fairy.

While waiting for Mammy, Nanna and I ate a slice of bread smeared with Nestle's Milk. After supping a pot of tea, I tried to get the fire lit. Johnson's had delivered 2cwt of 'nutty slack' that week so at least for the next few days we would be cosy. I bashed the ashes flat with the shovel, set alight a fistful of sticks, slung on some coal, then held the draw-tin up to the opening. Soon the welcome sound of crackling wood filled the room.

According to Nanna's clock it was now five thirty. The fire was blazing and the wireless was blabbering away to itself on the sideboard.

I wondered what Nanna's eldest son Harold would have done if he could have seen how we lived. He owned his own home, just down the road from us, plus the cottage next door and had a thriving confectioners business in the centre of Marsden. During the last few years earlier he'd had several substantial pools wins – the latest being as much as two thousand eight hundred and fourteen pounds.

Granted, he had given Nanna a pound note out of his winnings and every Christmas he sent up a food parcel; jam, biscuits, a tin of ham, that kind of thing, but never once did he come and visit. I'd often thought it was strange how only Nanna's eldest and youngest children survived the in-between ones, all nine of them, died from various illnesses at early ages. Perhaps things would have been different if they'd lived.

At ten to six I went out, a shivering reindeer on the causeway, watching for Mammy. Mr White, the lamp lighter, had already passed by with his ladder, and was probably down Reddisher Road and well on his way to Marsden. The gaslamp above Private Road threw a halo over where th'up bus would stop. The moon was being unfriendly, so apart from the gas lamp and the soft shimmer of candlelight shining through our windows, only headlamps from an occasional car or lorry disturbed the darkness.

Pacing up and down like a frustrated sheepdog, I blew hot, excited breath on my numb paws. Through the dimness, I spotted lights feeling their way up Manchester Road; th'up bus was coming. It pulled into the kerb opposite and through its windows I could see that a couple of passengers were ready to get off – one of whom must surely be Mammy. The single decker rumbled up the hill, leaving two shadows walking away from the bus stop. I squinted to pick them out; Jean Woodward and Little Tommy. But where was Mammy? Perhaps she was walking up or coming in a taxi. As my goosebumps grew and there was still no sign of her, I just knew she'd forgotten. When the seven o'clock th'up bus came and went without her, my butterflies went back to sleep. It was either stay at home and get into bother on Monday, or dash to Marsden quicker than a lava flow and explain my lateness to Miss Theaker. Torn between school and Mammy, Mammy won.

"Never 'eed," smiled Nanna. "Stop 'ere n' keep me company." It wasn't that I wanted to leave Nanna on her own, but the bright lights of Parochial Hall beckoned like Nutwood. Our candle was down to the size of a thimble and the fire was nothing more than a few black cinders. As I flopped back onto the sofa, my reindeer outfit lost its magic…

I didn't see Mammy at all over Christmas and the nearest we came to celebrating it was looking through a pile of old cards that Little Tommy had given us. But around noon one Saturday, early in the New Year, she began hammering on the door like a pneumatic drill. We soon guessed, by the smell of the abuse firing through the letterbox, that she'd been drinking – probably VP wine with Topczewski.

"H'open this f------ door!" she demanded. "I want t'see my daughter!"

Graham, who had seen her staggering up the road and had locked the door well before she arrived, shouted "Tha mart as weell go wom because tha nut cumin' in 'ere wen tha's been suppin'!"

"Yer bastards," she hissed. "H'open this bloody door er else ah'll kick it down."

I ran to the flock tickin and curled up beside my Nanna. The sleeve of Kathleen's coat poked out from under the pillow. Mammy began booting the bottom of the door and I jumped at each thud. She might actually break in and drag me off to live with her and The Goblin. I clung tight to Nanna while Graham paced the floor. But the booting and the banging, and the various slurred expletives continued for some time. Eventually she must have tired. After a defiant kick all went quiet.

"'as she gone?" I whispered to Graham. Quietly he tiptoed across the oilcloth to the window.

"Yus, it's alreit," he replied. "Ah can see 'er walkin' down t'rooad."

Nanna breathed a sigh of relief as I jumped off the bed to join Graham. His mop of coal hair flopped untidily.

"That woman's du-lally," he declared – "bloody du-lally!" I couldn't have agreed more, but seeing her zigzagging down the pavement, no doubt muttering incoherent oaths to herself, it suddenly struck me how lonely she looked. Her pin-sized head disappeared beneath the large collar of a shabby, jumble sale mink coat, and her spidery legs half hidden beneath its hem made me desperately wish that we'd let her in.

PART 3

CHAPTER EIGHT

SPRING '57

Around that time, our Arnold came back up Standedge, but still seemed to only be around at night. Unlike me, who always curled up beneath the itchy blanket and tattered old coat with my Nanna, Arnold slept in the most uncomfortable places. Many a night he'd curl up like a cat on the hearthrug or lay prostrate in the middle of the floor. Sometimes he would sleep on the horsehair couch, sometimes roll into a ball at the foot of our bed. Icy winds galloped across the moor, rapped on our door and rattled our windowpanes. They howled down our chimney and swept in underneath the threshold. Vicious draughts charged round our house, every crack and gap poked by frozen fingers, and never did I see Arnold with a cushion or a pillow, nor a sheet or a blanket.

After the winds, frosts would arrive leaving a curtain of ice as thick on the inside of our windows as out. It nipped our fingers and pinched our toes raw. But muffling Arnold up in a dressing gown and slippers would have smothered him. It wouldn't have matched his identity either, for Arnold's new name was Strong – John Strong.

"Yer can't call yerself that," I said one morning whilst sliding down the stairs on my bottom.

"Why not?" asked Arnold.

"Cos yer CAN'T change yer name, yer not allowed."

Arnold ignored me.

Sometimes Arnold would go to school, and sometimes he wouldn't. It took cunning to hide from Mr Carter the schoolboard man. Arnold would sneak around Marsden like a common thief, nipping behind thick hedges and high walls. It didn't take him long to realise that if the school bobby was waiting at Nanna's, Manchester Road was far too exposed to make a quick getaway. A better approach, he told me, was from behind on Waters Road. If he succeeded in getting this far, he could then creep up Private Road and lurk behind a tree. If Mr. Carter's vehicle was nowhere in sight he would burst into Nanna's grinning from ear to ear.

One day, when mizzly dampness had replaced the frost, Arnold grabbed his herrycart and set off for a scrat around on Flint's Tip.

"Can I cum, can I cum?" I leapt like a flame around him.

"No, yer'll be in t'way."

"No ah won't. Please Arnie, let me cum."

He groaned and gave in. "If yer any bother, ah'm sending yer 'ome. And it in't Arnie, it's John."

Flint's Tip was on the side of the road, sandwiched between Mrs Schofield's cottage and the Coach and Horses. The Belgi firm dumped rubbish here as well as the farm and Arnold came once a week to sling stones at rats, and see what he could salvage. It smelt of rotten rags. We dug around in the cinders and chunks of brittle onyx, trying to find treasure. "These were found buried at the bottom of the sea," smirked Arnold, hauling out old bottles. "Pulled from the wreckage of a ship sunk by pirates. The sailors went down wi' their rum."

"This little fat 'un 'ad Bovril in it," I said, wiping the muck down the front of my cardigan.

Arnold had put the bottles down and was heaving out pram wheels. "Snapped clean off the 'errycart of Blind Bob as 'e cum flyin' down Manchester Road from t'cuttin', crashed into t'wall and tumbled down there." He pointed down the steep drop to the stream. "Rest of 'is cart were never found. Nor were 'is body. But ah'm 'avin' 'is wheels." Arnold flung them onto his own herrycart.

"Look Arnie," I cried, snatching up shiny chips and dropping them like green hailstones on some soggy cardboard. "Emeralds."

"Don't be daft. Them's glass, so don't cut yerself."

There was treasure everywhere, from yellowing rags that had once been golden robes, to gleaming silver spokes, lucky stones[*] and chunks of obsidian coal. I found an old tin crusted with amber, and some jagged amber amulets to match. Arnold had no use for these (apart from the coal) so he kicked them away and became interested instead in an old jam jar which would do, he said, to keep his nails in.

I helped him roll a huge tyre to the herrycart, we tipped it over and it fell with a thunk, making the cart jerk alarmingly. It would be fun to bully the tyre down the field when we got home. Arnold's best treasure was an old bed iron.

"Ah can build a shed wi' that," he decided.

It was a right effort to pull the stuff home, even down the hill, because of the topsy-turvy way the cart was loaded. The sticking out bed frame kept bashing our legs.

Back outside th'owd 'ouse, we unloaded our fortune.

"We're rich," I said.

"Ah'm gunner mek summet wi' these 'ere wheels," Arnold said.

---

[*] *Pieces of unatural stone created from the time the Standedge tunnel system was blasted out. They are usually smooth turquoise chunks streaked with blues and greys. To us they represented something magic.*

One morning whilst out searching for excitement he came across a Cuts and Fletcher's coal wagon. It had overturned by the 'Two Police'.[*]

"Will yer ever drive agen?" He asked the shocked driver as he shovelled lumps of coal off the road and into one of our galvanized buckets.

On another occasion a sudden cold snap had left the road like a toboggan run, vehicles were slipping and sliding everywhere. One of them, a lorry carrying Eveready Batteries, skidded on a patch of ice below the Motorman's Café. Arnold was soon there poking his nose in. "Will yer ever drive agen?" He asked the haulier, as he, and two other men, heaved and pushed and shoved until the wagon was back on its wheels. He was repaid for his effort with an Eveready battery to fit our flashlight.

His capers didn't stop at helping people either. One mild February day he decided he'd build himself a house. The foundation stones were already laid, in the form of a shepherd's shelter that lay skeletal out on the moor. "You'll never build a 'ouse," I snorted.

"Ah built an 'en 'ut didn't ah?" He replied.

I watched him load our long tin bath onto his herrycart, and when he'd cadged one shilling and sixpence off Nanna, scooted off to Marsden dragging the herrycart behind him. He was on his way to Chadwick's where he'd often popped in for bits of chicken wire, staples, nails or a handful of putty. When he returned puffing and sweating, his bathtub was filled up with Blue Mortar. Arnold

---

[*] *A lane leading to Tunnel End and so named because the stone pillars standing at either side looked like two policemen.*

intended to cement his walls together. I trotted alongside, on his final stage of the journey, a drag across the moor to the building site. On arrival at the plot, we were both dismayed to find that the tub of Blue Mortar had set like concrete.

"Never mind," he said and turned his attentions to making money. His schemes were as varied as his sleeping arrangements and included the following list:

EMPLOYER	JOB REQUIREMENTS	RATES
Kenneth Warhurst	Feed Hens	1 Gill of milk in Billy Can
Mr, Mrs Bray	Open gate for car	Sixpence
Miss Billcliffe	Shovel manure out of mistle	A penny a pile

It didn't take long for him to realise that he'd make more by selling things. So less than three months after he'd got his bike, he started doing away with it, bit by bit. If it had been my bike, I'd have looked after it like it was a 'norse', polishing it up and riding it as much as possible. But with Arnold it was as battle scarred as an old warship. Islands of maroon paint, scratched and scored, floated around on a chrome sea dotted with rust. Around its wheels, clumps of dried mud clung like mattings of muck trawling the underbellies of sheep.

Late one afternoon there was a knock on the door. Arnold, who was sitting on the couch polishing a wheel hub he'd found in the gutter, jumped up to answer it. The grey suited man glaring down at us announced himself as the manager of Harrop's in Huddersfield. He had a fancy moustache that twitched irritably as he made inquiries about the bike. Arnold, unconcerned, led him down the slippery steps of the gable end, along the narrow passageway and into the owd 'ouse. I ran along after them.

It was blacker than Topczewski's trilby in the tumbledown cottage, until the manager lit up a Swan Vesta, nearly catching the flame on his powdery blue tie. From the beams, dusty cobwebs hung like lace doilys. Bits of scrap metal and rusty tools lay abandoned on the floor. Paper curled off damp walls – a reminder of past occupancy. The past occupant, a neat French lady, had long since given way to the ancient smell and Graham's junk. A strange gurgle escaped from the manager's throat. In the centre of all this chaos was the bike, upturned like a dead dinosaur, stripped of mudguards, wheels and brake cables.

"Is this the bike your mother bought from Harrops?" Glowered the manager through the matchlight. Mammy had bought it on the tick and was probably behind with the payments.

"Yes," replied Arnold.

"Is it all here?"

"Yes." Arnold lied. The manager glared at him in disbelief, and in the last glimmer of light dropped the matchstick carelessly on the step beneath him, turned on his heels and marched off.

Arnold couldn't have cared less who were the legal owners of the bike. The minute he was offered one pound ten shillings for it from a boy up Hard End, he waved it goodbye without as much as a bye-or-leave, and darted off to Frank Mayle's Sweet Shop, where he frittered his brass on a bag of torpedoes, some pineapple chunks and a quarter of Jap Desserts in sugar coating, which he was reluctant to share.

Mammy, who was still lumbered with the HP, tried unsuccessfully to get the bike back. The boy's father, a big Irish Navvy, just laughed in her face.

Divvy Day was one of the most exciting events down in the village. It was curious to watch how the divvy receipts arrived. Often I'd stood at the counter with a bag of sugar and watched the money suck up the tube to the Co-op counting house. Moments later, change, if there was any, and the tiny slip of paper printed with our divvy number saying what we'd spent would drop down. These divvy receipts were too small to go on the foot high spike Nanna told us to skewer our other receipts on, so they went in a tin box, and when it was nearly time, Nanna reckoned up how many tanners we'd get back.

You could do what Doris Iredale did, and have your divvy paid into your Co-op share book, or the Post Office, but we always got cash back to buy in.

I trotted down Waters Road, basket in one hand, divvy number and shopping list in the other and my mouth watering at the thought of Turog smeared with Kraft margarine and Hartleys jam. What a good meal that would make us all. And for tea, Lin Can peas and boiled ham, washed down with dandelion and burdock from a glass bottle with a stopper.

By the time I reached the village, everybody was obviously in the same mind. Marsdeners swarmed along Towngate, on Market Place, down Peel Street and up Brougham Road. Farmers with fuzzy beards, waspy old women with baskets, Louie Schofield huddled over like a furry bee picking at something out of a shopping bag. Boys with grasshopper legs leapt out of Frank Mayles with bulging pockets, and I waved at Little Tommy who was heading for Manchester Road for th'up bus. Mrs Dearnley was outside Moorhouses, talking to Teddy Hellawell. She smiled and said hello.

A familiar face passed by, humming to themselves, and someone else I saw a lot, but didn't know, flew along, disappearing resolutely into Johnsons. It was like Christmas Eve, but warmer. All Marsden was buzzing, and the Co-op office on Brougham Road was honey.

I flitted in amongst bags and chatter, and hovered in the doorway before deciding to save the excitement for last, and pop into Nellie's first for candles.

Nellie Beardsall had kept her shop for years and years and years, and according to Nanna it hadn't altered any. Nellie was in her mid-fifties, and stood behind her counter amongst a confusion of bootlaces, Mansion polish, buckets, brushes, and mops. Our Graham had bought a tilly lamp from here one time, and had to carry home the Esso Blue paraffin for it in a glass Ben Shaws pop bottle.

As Nellie wrapped my candles up into a paper parcel, I tried to pick out the faded lettering on mantles packed flat in cellophane. I couldn't wait to get out and away from the smell of blacklead and soot, and fly up the steps to the Co-op offices.

I eagerly handed in the slip with our divvy number on. A young woman studied the ledger in front of her, already open, for several minutes.

"2166," she frowned. "You sure?"

I nodded, impatient to taste the arrowroot biscuits on the list.

"Sorry 2166 has already been cashed. Did no-one at home tell you?"

No-one at home knew.

It was a long way to the bottom of the stairs. No special fig biscuits for Nanna. No jam for tea. No sticky treacle. It was an even longer journey home.

When Nanna saw my empty basket, she didn't even need to ask. She sank back down onto her pillow sighing, "Kitty's cashed us divvy."

CHAPTER NINE

SPRING '57

It wasn't long before Mammy was in another drunken tizz. This time she turned up on the doorstep just after three-thirty one morning, held in place by two policemen. "Found her curled up in a phone box," they said, "told us she had nowhere else to sleep. She gave us this address, is it ok if she stays till morning?"

We all hung in the doorway, bleared with sleep and bewildered by being banged out of it by persistant knocking. "Ah suppose it'll 'ave t'be," Graham grunted, glaring at Mammy through the candleflame.

"She'll 'ave been drinkin' wine wi' that Topczweski agen," critisised Nanna as the taller of the two policemen deposited Mammy unceremoniously onto the couch. Without coat and dressed only in a light summer frock, Mammy slouched awkwardly in one corner, a discarded daisy with her head bent. No one thought to cover her up. Even if we had, there were no spare blankets.

"Gets drunk regular, does she?" asked the shorter of the officers.

"She's a bloody nuisance," growled Graham.

"Well, when she sobers up, tell her next time she fancies spending the night outdoors to either wrap up warm or wait 'til summer."

Graham clomped upstairs. Nanna took a deep breath, and I began tossing and turning on the lumpy tickin.

I hoped nobody at school would find out about this. The voices of Doreen Daws and Carol Greenwood suddenly seemed loud in my ears, "Yer mother's a drunken wi-itch, yer mother's a drunken wi-itch."

It seemed strange to waken up in the morning with Mammy there, I must have dreamed she'd got on her broomstick and flown off. I got up first, still wearing what I'd had on since Christmas, my throat feeling as if it had swallowed a scouring pad. Graham was having his usual Sunday morning 'lig-in[*] and Nanna was awake but not talking. Arnold might have spent the night at Daisy Abbiss's.[**] She liked Arnold; thought of him as a stray cat who needed taking in and feeding sometimes.

Mammy being there was the only difference in my routine. I had neither comb nor toothbrush, so just swilled my hands and face quickly in cold water

---

[*] *Lie in.*

[**] *An ex-evacuee from London who had lived at Nanna's during the war. She'd enjoyed village life so much she'd bought a little house on Warrington Terrace and settled there.*

poured from the bucket we'd fetched last night.

As I stepped outside with the bucket, ready for traipsing up to the well, for this morning's fresh water, I could hear Mammy stirring. I hoped I wouldn't be returning to another row. Happen she'd leave before Graham got up.

At 7am Manchester Road was deserted. After a quick glance in both directions I slipped across and headed for the footpath. I was careful where I walked as both my shoes had holes in. The bits of cardboard I'd stuffed inside were war n' wuz.* Settling down my pail beneath the spring, I made myself as comfortable as possible on a large round boulder and waited for it to fill. Somewhere in the distance a dog barked and sheep bleated. As the silver water trickled into my battered bucket, a solitary car crept down the road like a shiny fish. The sprawling landscape stretched before me like an emerald ocean.

Beneath the wild moorland, dry stone walls divided irregular meadows. Tucked into the Pennine slopes, Riley's farmhouse was coming to life, plumes of smoke curling from its tall chimneystack. The most prominent farm was Flint's, whose walls and solid outbuildings towered above everything else on Marsden's western horizon. It was George Flint's sheep which roamed around Marsden.

The hills above Eastergate were wearing March clothes, and in the valley bottom twiggy sycamores were laden with buds. To my left, but hidden from view was Pule Hill under which ran the Rochdale Canal and a railway tunnel. Around it an old Roman road and a packhorse trail twisted and turned to Lancashire. We'd learnt about 'Blind Jack' Metcalf of Knaresborough at school, the man who had laid out a road fit for coaches through part of the village. It had come down Chain Road, straight down Brougham Road, through Towngate in the

---

* *Worse than anything, any old how.*

centre of Marsden, turning southwards up Throstle Nest and west again over Standedge. Manchester Road, as it was as I filled my bucket, had been built in1839.

Soon it would be summer and I expected that busloads of folk would appear the first hot weekend. It was the stream at Eastergate that was the main attraction I'd heard Little Tommy's wife say it was as busy as Blackpool prom on August bank holiday, as grown ups and their noisy children tramped in their fashionable sunsuits and gaudy shorts across my territory. Graham didn't share my view. Last year I'd seen him sitting on the grass up Eastergate with some lads and lasses. Loud music had blasted from a wind up gramaphone and their raucous laughter frightened the sheep.

I picked up my bucket and turned for home. A playful wind, which normally wouldn't have bothered me, suddenly caused me to shiver. My throat felt even sorer and my arms and legs ached. But, like Arnold, I wasn't in the habit of staying indoors and complaining.

When I got back home, Mammy was standing by the door with the slop bucket, just about to teem the disgusting contents down the outside drain.

"I'll put t'kettle on in a minute" she croaked. She looked as rough as I felt.

By the middle of the week I felt worse. What had begun with a sore throat had developed into a barking cough. I sneezed constantly and my nose was as red as the reindeer I should have played in the pantomime.

"Yer'll 'ave t'see a doctor t'night" Nanna frowned as I rubbed my nose down my cardigan sleeve, "er else yer gunner end up wi' newmonia. Call in on yer way 'ome from school. 'is surgery's at top a' drive next t'County School."

It was coming dusk as I approached the surgery but a welcoming light shone through what was presumably the waiting room window. I had never been to a doctor's before so I opened the door and stepped cautiously into a dismal room with a polished table standing in the middle of it. On top lay a few women's magazines and an aspidistra like Nanna's – only this one, according to its shiny leaves, had been dusted. I didn't know what to do next, so I tiptoed to a heavy wooden bench and sat silently down near an old man and woman, both glanced up at me, but said nothing. There was a sign that said *'coughs and sneezes spread diseases, wrap them in your handkerchief'*. My handkerchief had become Violet's face.

Through a door to my right I could hear low voices. Must be where the doctor was – I'd seen something similar in a book at school. After a few minutes I began to feel bored but the only things I dared to move were my eyes. If I rolled them round and squinted sideways I could observe my neighbours without being seen. The woman, like me, was sitting stiff as a poker. On her feet I spied a pair of black suede shoes and dark stockings that didn't wrinkle. The gentleman beside her looked equally smart. I couldn't see his face but noticed that his shoes were well heeled and he had sharp creases down the front of his trousers. I suddenly became conscious of my own footwear. They had looked quite decent when I'd bought them from the jumble sale, but now the wet got in and their champagne uppers had become badly worn. What I would have liked was a brand new pair of sandals from the shoe department at the Co-op. During the summer I'd seen some on display in the window. They'd had white crepe soles and a fancy pattern stamped out of the leather below the T strap, similar to Kathleen's, only hers had been red: whereas I would have chosen brown ones. Two years earlier Nanna had reluctantly made me wear Kathleen's. I would have preferred not to. They had been on her feet the night she ran under the lorry, and beside the buckle on the right sandal the leather was ripped, making it slack. Every time I fastened it, Kathleen's pale face and horrific injuries jumped out at me.

Doctor Hande, the one who had given Kathleen emergency treatment that night, was now standing at the surgery door smiling at me. All that shifty squinting at other people's shoes had left me with a headache.

"Come in… come in," the doctor said, guiding me through with an extended arm. Then pointing to a chair in front of his desk he told me to sit down.

"Now what seems to be the matter, Heather? It is Heather isn't it?"

"Yes." I answered quietly. "Ah've got a cowd on mi chest."

"I see," he said standing up and putting both ends of his stethoscope into his ears. "Now breathe in… And out… Say argh… Good, good. You've got an ear and throat infection," he concluded. "I'll prescribe you some medicine. Er… where's your Mother tonight by the way?"

He sat down and began fiddling with his fountain pen.

"Ah don't know," I answered truthfully.

"Well next time you visit me," he continued, "you must come with an adult."

I felt stupid and felt myself go red. But at least the medicine was worth the visit. It tasted of raspberries.

A few nights later I was running down the road to the Motorman's Café feeling much better, when through the gaslight emerged Mammy. She was in a mad ig.*

"Wat the bloody 'ell 'ave you been t'doctor's for?" she boomed. Before I had time to answer she continued "'e's just been t'our house n' played 'oly 'ell wi' me! 'ow the 'ell am ah supposed t'know there's owt up wi' yer h'if yer don't tell me, yer silly little bitch! Yer just tryin' t' get me into bother h'arn't yer! Well ah can tell yer now ah'm not 'avin' that sort er work."

I was so suprised by this attack, I couldn't speak. (I was glad there was no one around to hear her). Wasn't it her responsibility to ensure I was all right not

---

* *Temper.*

my responsibility to make sure she was?

"H'if they put yer in a *Home* yer've only yerself t'blame!" she stormed. She spun round and stomped off.

The day finally came for school medicals. I'd been playing rounders outside during P.T, and was unable to slog the ball like I normally did because of the impending embarrassment.

I joined the queue of boys and girls wearing vests and liberty bodices in various shades of white or grey, depending on the hygiene of their mothers. Mine was nearly black. The queue shrank and I shrank with it, each step towards the doctor, a step nearer doom.

Then there I was, face to face with the man who pulled me towards him by my skinny wrist, a contrast to that of round Pauline Hill who was now running back to get dressed.

He pushed his cold stethoscope up the back of my bodice. "Breathe in…" he ordered "and out." Then he moved round the front. I cringed. He could have played a xylophone on my ribs with his stethoscope. After peering in my ears and squinting down my throat, he had a long, stern stare, then asked what I'd had for breakfast.

My jaw dropped. "A boiled egg," I lied, remembering Mammy's earlier outburst.

٣

CHAPTER TEN

SUMMER '57

When summer arrived, sharras passed on their way to Blackpool. Bloomin' day-trippers appeared - on th'up bus every hot weekend. But at least with brighter days and lighter nights there was less groveling around in the dark searching for candles, the lack of coal was not such a problem, and food seemed less important. Fetching water in deep snow was put aside for at least six months and life was a bit nicer.

"Th'up Bus"

And what was summer for, but for tramping across the moor in search of birds' nests. I rarely found one, and when I did it was usually empty. The hunt was so exciting, it was always worth it. Once in a while I did discover eggs, Meadow Pipits or Skylarks, and extracted them from their hidey-holes as if they were wounded Imps of Spring.[*] They were the same shape as the oveletts we burnt at home if Nanna was flush. Rare as finding eggs! I lowered them back onto their bed of sticks, vowing to return when they hatched – but with the birth of other plans, I never did.

In our playground, we'd stopped skipping and playing hopscotch because everyone was bringing in hula-hoops instead. About the size of cart wheels these large rings of ribbed plastic came in pea green, egg yellow, mauve, blue and raspberry red. Russell's Toy Shop sold them for as cheap as one shilling and sixpence. I never had one myself but enjoyed twirling Margaret Hoppers around my waist. Being thin as a latt and wick as a weasel it was usually me who kept it spinning the longest.

---

[*] *Characters from Rupert The Bear.*

It was nice to see flowers unfurling again, painting a rainbow onto the stormy sea up Standedge. Garden flowers, wild flowers, weeds, I didn't mind. My favourite was Pink Purslane, which I first discovered out stickin' down Private Road. The sudden splash of colour amongst brown earth and dried leaves took my breath, like meeting a lady dressed for a wedding on the windy moor. I crouched there motionless, studying each petal ranging in colour from pale mauve to rich purple. Pink Purslane didn't flaunt itself like other flowers, but hid, modest behind a sycamore tree.

I could only identify common flowers. Polianthus was one of them. Little Tommy had given me one to plant in a small patch of earth next to our outside lavatory.

"It's called a POLIANTHUS." He'd spelt it out slowly so I wouldn't forget.

I liked Little Tommy; I liked his wrinkled brow and his smiling eyes. Sunflowers grew taller than him! Under his guidance I'd planted the shoots. I'd waited, watched and watered till finally two blooms burst out deep indigo round centres of sunshine. But that had been back in spring.

In our classroom the nature table was full of summer stuff: pink and white daisies, silverweed and shepherd's purse. Pat and Joan had even gathered Harebells. (One flower I never picked, was Wild Carrot – or Mother-Die. Mammy had once told me that if I were to pick this it would kill her! She didn't say how. But having already felt responsible for 'making summet 'appen' once in my life, I certainly wasn't going to risk doing it again.)

Pink Purslane

Nicholas had brought in a beautiful, but dead, butterfly. Although papery thin wings gleamed with bronze, tipped with red and spotted white were fully open, it was hard to believe this perfectly healthy looking little creature was dead. But dead it was and Miss Woffenden had labelled it 'RED ADMIRAL'. That summer, Brian and his twin brother Michael, had been to the seaside. They'd returned with a pile of pebbles and a bucket full of shells. When I told Nanna about the shells she said that if I put one to my ear, I would be able to hear the sea.

My own contribution to the table was a fist full of sheep's wool which I'd found entangled around a fence post on my way to school. It was thick and matted like the carpet in Margaret Hopper's house. Miss Woffenden wrote 'RAW WOOL' on a piece of paper beneath it.

One of my favourite places during that summer was Marsden Park.[*] Although right next to Manchester Road, once you were through the big iron gates, secret nooks and secluded seats hid amongst a maze of narrow pathways and rows of Rhododendron bushes and speckled laurel. The best time to explore it was early evening around four thirty. When most people were eating their tea, I'd be hanging about the bandstand jumping up and down the stone steps waiting for the Crown Green Bowlers to leave.

Right next to the green was a tennis court where young men and women in dazzling white shorts bounded about. They all looked rather posh to me and I was glad when they packed up their rackets and left me alone. Sometimes I'd sneak around the perimeter of the park, or follow one of the little wandering paths that led up to, and behind, the war memorial. Having the park to myself was creepy and exciting, like being a cat burglar about to pinch Annuals from Russell's.

I was never entirely alone though. Parties of sandy-coated brown-capped sparrows, bobbed about in the shrubbery. Every now and then one or two would hop onto the path beside me, looking for crumbs. Blackbirds were forever gathering bits of dried grass and sticks.

Sometimes I would pretend the rockeries were cliffs to scramble up (minding the plants), and the gaps in holly bushes secret dens with treasure hidden in there by smugglers, just right for me to crawl into.

It was after one such visit to the park that I got caught in a thunderstorm. It had been a sticky day and even I, who usually did everything at a gallop, had slowed to a trot. But it wasn't until I left the park and headed for home that I began to realise that I might get wet. The belly of thunder rumbled louder and the sky overhead began to darken. A sudden breeze brushed the air, causing a litter of dead leaves to sweep along the pavement. By the time I reached Peel Street rain was bouncing off the flagstones. This sudden downfall sent folk scurrying into shops whilst others sheltered in doorways. Some people were already prepared and shook out black or brown Pacamac's, thin coats and umbrellas. Despite only wearing a short sleeved frock, I splashed through whatever puddle was in front of me.

Suddenly, a hand of lightning grabbed the church tower, twisted fingers pointing at the gravestones. It was followed by an earth-shattering bang, which seemed to rock the very foundations of the Co-op. The louder it cracked the better I liked it.

The thunderstorm lasted for a good half-hour, and by the time I reached Private Road End the sun had come back out. A damp, earthy smell filled the air. All along the lane, wet dandelions glittered in the sunshine, like Nanna's favourite brooch. Trees dripped.

The thunderstorm had been thrilling. I had felt safer outdoors than I would

[*] *Built around 1912 and paid for by local mill owners.*

have in. Mammy had once told me that if a thunderbolt should came down our chimney it would probably kill us. My eyes had widened as she'd reeled off horrendous tales of people struck down while safe at home.

"T'prevent this," she'd added, "h'it's h'important t'keep t'door h'open, then t'bolt er thunder'll pass straight through t' 'ouse and out a t'door. "

I'd been looking forward to sports day for ages. Winning races was fun and everyone congratulated you, and it was so nice to get out of a stuffy classroom. When sports day actually came, so did heat spots, red and raw all over the soles of my feet. That should be no bother though, I was faster than anyone in my class, and heatspots or no heatspots, I would prove it.

All morning I stamped my feet to stop them itching, kicking one foot hard against the other. Pain was better than itching, I thought, till the spots stopped itching and became angry. Other people used Calamine Lotion to cool them. I'd seen it in bottles in the chemists, like pink milk.

But I could cope with heatspots this summer like every other summer. So with Nanna's advice ringing in my ears, "Don't scrat em love, yer'll mek em worse," I just imagined them away, and that worked till dinner time when I had to leave my seat.

After dinner, the whole school traipsed up Fall Lane, and all the way up Mount Road to the cricket field. One teacher led and another hung back. Everyone else walked in pairs.

"What's wrong wi' yer feet 'eather?" Asked Margaret Hopper, as I limped across the street with her by the crossroads in my badly fitting shoes.

"Nowt much," I said, trying and failing to ignore the pain.

"Yer can't run like that," whispered Margaret.

"Watch me," I said.

And she watched me finish last.

All in all it had been a good summer. Mammy had even managed to remember my 8th birthday. I was in class at the time, sitting at my little wooden desk reciting 'The Fairies' by William Allingham.

Up the airy mountain,
Down the rushy glen,
We daren't go a-hunting
For fear of little men;
Wee folk, good folk,
Trooping all together;
Green jacket, red cap,
And white owl's feather!

I had just made my mind up to memorise it for Nanna when the double doors creaked behind me. Seeing the flash of black hair and blue plastic beach shoes step inside, I shrank into my seat. Mammy – who else, all dressed up in a bright turquoise frock with a rim of black velvet running around its hem, rouge daubed on her cheeks and that familiar diamante hairgrip. She was clutching a brown paper bag. She spied me out, and beckoned me towards her.

By now the whole class had swiveled their heads round, glancing at her, then me. Mr Cheatham, who was standing beside the blackboard with the poetry book in his hand, indicated that I could go and talk to her. I pushed back my chair, trying not to scrape it, and shuffled towards her.

"H'ave brought yer summet fer yer birthday," she barked (in a voice which she probably thought only I could hear.) "Ah know yer'll like it... it's got a h'animal on it."

My birthday had been three weeks earlier. It had passed unnoticed and I was beginning to wish it had remained that way. She handed me the crumpled bag. Not wishing to appear ungrateful I opened it and peered in, then shut it together again with a loud crunch. I had just made out two little glass bowls of white sand fastened to the curly head of a plastic poodle.

"It's a h'egg timer," Mammy confirmed, giving me a toothless smile. "Ah saw it in t' greengrocer's winder n' thought yer'd like it."

"Thank you," I murmured, "It's lov'ly... Erm... ah... ah'd better go now... we're readin' poytry."

Mammy looked pleased and treated me to another gummy grin. As I made my way back to my desk I could hear her banging shut the double doors.

As I sank back into my seat, Vivian, who was sitting next to me, whispered, "Wat's in t'bag, 'eather?"

I was going to have to say something.

"Mi birthday present."

"Wor is it?

"Yer've t'guess," I said, stalling for time.

"Wat's it begin wi?"

Two more girls who were sitting behind me had also joined in the whispering.

"Be quiet!" Snapped Mr Cheatham. "Heather, stop turning round and look at page twenty one."

"Wat's it begin wi'?" hissed Vivian when he was facing the board again.

"Erm...E.T." I said. No one – absolutely no one could possibly guess such a ridiculously silly birthday present beginning with E.T.

"Egg timer," shouted Joan from behind.

The next time Miss Newton came poking her nose in, she asked if I'd enjoyed my birthday. I glanced at my egg timer on the dusty sideboard and just nodded. She'd said little else, and after she'd gone, Nanna remembered we'd no bread in.

"Can ah 'ave a packet o' crisps as well, Nanna?" I asked hopefully.

Nanna said that I could, but I was to watch the road and come straight home. She knew only too well that I had a habit of setting off and not returning until dusk. The first time that I'd done it she had been beside herself with worry. She had even climbed out of bed and stood by the window watching anxiously for my return.

"Ah've been at me wit's end wi' worry," she'd cried as I'd ran in, unconcerned about the coming dark. But I had no conception of time and came and went just as I pleased, and climbed into bed whenever I felt like it.

I did watch the road, then ran along the grass verge. The Motorman's Café was a minute's walk in the direction of Marsden, and a favourite stopping place for long distance drivers. It was here that the unfortunate lorry driver from Hyde in Cheshire had stopped for a bite to eat just over four years ago. Nanna had always blamed him for staying too long at the Café, then rushing to get home.

Despite its immense size, the Café clung to the side of the moor as if seeking protection. The large semi-circle car park was infested with potholes. Each week a lorry load of cinders was brought up from the Gas 'ole* in Marsden and tipped into them. Graham sometimes took a bucket down and picked bits of coke out of the cinders. These were called clinkers, and were very hard to find, but it was worth the effort, for once they were alight they glowed like a furnace and burnt for hours.

Mr. and Mrs. Morley, who kept the Café, were a kind couple. They sold milk, cakes and hot meat and potato pies to the neighbouring cottagers. The appertizing smell of bacon and eggs, fried bread, chips and sausages oozing from inside were enough to make my mouth water. The most we ever bought from the café though, was a loaf of bread, a packet of Smith's crisps or a cream bun, but sometimes I bought my sweets from there. Nanna like their boiled sweets best – Yorkshire Mixtures and yellow striped humbugs.

That particular day Mrs Iredale had been cooking a ham shank for her customers.

"'ere yer are, love" she said, passing me a lumpy parcel wrapped in newspaper. "There's some 'am bones in 'ere wi' plenty o' meat on. Tek em 'ome fer yer Nanna, ah'm sure she'll enjoy em. They'll do 'er good - like, build 'er up."

The bones were still warm. I ran straight home with them and showed them to Nanna. She was every bit as pleased as I had expected.

"Put 'em in a pan on t'stove, love" she smiled, "'alf full t'pan wi' water n' put a pinch o' salt in. They'll make a nice bit o' broth. When they start t'boil turn t'gas down n' let em simmer."

Whilst this scrumptious meal bubbled and gurgled on the low heat and

---

* *The small Gas Works.*

wafted the most delicious smell through the rooms of Millstone Cottage, I sprawled full length on the rag rug and made up a poem. 'Up down up down' – I wrote on one of the pages of Graham's Filmgoers Diary – 'I'd like to meet the funniest clown'.

"Listen t'this, Nanna" I said, jumping to my feet and bounding over to the bed, "Ah've made it up mi sen, do yer like it?"

Nanna said it was very good, but what would Graham have to say when he saw that I'd been scribbling in his diary?

"Ah 'aven't been scribblin', Nanna." I said, mortified, "It's mi best 'andwriting,"

Nanna said, "It doesn't matter what your 'andwriting's like, it's still Graham's diary and he might not want poymes in it!"

"Ah'll only write one more then" I said. "You recite one n' ah'll write it down."

Autumn crept across Millstone Cottages, as the year, like Nanna, grew older. Sun still managed to filter through our grimy windowpanes, but without all the yellow urgency of a dandelion. It had tuned watery, a pale primrose slowly fading.

CHAPTER ELEVEN

WINTER '57- UP TO CHRISTMAS

PEZ WILSON

The Iredales next door moved out, and went to live a bit further down the road opposite the Motorman's Café. Our new neighbours were a couple with a baby and a very loud wireless which went on into the night.

"They've getten Luxembourg on again," cried Graham, who could hear it through his bedroom wall.

One day I was playing with David Iredale who was a year younger than me, and as blonde as us Wainwrights were dark. He took me to his dad's garage, up a stony oily lane across from their new house.

"'ave a look at this," he said proudly. There, inside the garage was a huge motor car like a shiny black beetle, but with wheels not legs. There was also dark splotches on the floor, and the same greasy, creosoty smell that was in the 'owd 'ouse sometimes when Graham was nakklin' with some old motor cycle.

"In't it nice?" crowed David. "Ah can drive it, yer know. Mi dad taught me. Do yer want me t'tek yer fer a ride?"

He didn't need to ask twice. I pushed in the handle and the door swung open like a heavy wing. David set about 'startin' 'er up' and after some frightful noise, we drove right out of the garage and down the stony lane.

"Ooh David," I gasped in delight, "you are clever."

We reached Manchester Road, and he swung the car right, then cruised along downhill, coming to a stop outside their house. Just then, Joe Iredale came rushing out, and flung open the drivers' door pulling David out by his shirt collar, and dragging him round the front of the car, onto the pavement. I thought I'd better get out too. Joe was playing hell fire.

"What the bloody 'ell d'yer think yer doin', yer stupid little buggers. Yer could 'ave caused an accident. Yer could 'ave…yer could 'ave bin killed. You…" he pointed to me "Get off 'ome, an' you… yer bloody idiot," shoving poor David in the back "Get inside. Yer mother'll play 'oly 'ell."

I slunk back up the hill, wondering if David Iredale would ever drive again.

As the last leaves fell, we were once more faced with the fact that another long winter was about to begin. One Saturday evening in early December, Mammy paid us a visit and for once was behaving rationally. Graham had been playing 'Last train to San Fernando' for Nanna on his gramaphone, and had now put it all away and gone to Marsden Bug 'Ole* with his friend Barry Carter. Arnold had just dragged in a rusty pram he'd found on the tip. Nanna was sitting up in bed, talking to Mammy through the fireshine. On the sideboard two burning candles added extra warmth and for a bit things were pleasant enough, then I said to Arnold, "It's my turn to sit in't pram," but he'd made himself comfortable - sort of - shoes wedged tight at the bottom, refusing to budge.

"Come on, Arnie, you said we'd teck turns."

"I'm stayin' 'ere," said Arnold, firmly, folding his arms.

"T'int fair" I sniffed, and began to moan at him long and loud till he finally squeezed himself out, swung his grimy legs over the side and slid off.

"Ah've got pins an' needles anyway," he grumbled.

Being smaller, I fitted better. Grabbing what I thought reins might be, I galloped off down Private Road on my pram-'orse, urging it to go faster. I'd only been galloping two minutes when Arnold started shaking its rusty flank.

"Yer've 'ad enough now."

"No," I shrieked "I've only just got in."

"Well get out."

"You've 'ad longer n' me," I wailed.

"I'm older. Now shift yerself."

Arnold shook some more, not listening to my protests, then started trying to

---

* *Picture House.*

push me out; I shoved him back, and a scrap started.

We ignored Nanna's weak pleas of "For goodness sake stop fratchin'." Then suddenly she rose from her bed and made an agitated shuffle for the door. Arnold and I stopped.

"Where are yer goin'?" yelled Mammy, dashing after her. "Yer can't go h'out in this weather it'll kill yer!"

"Let it!" Cried Nanna "Ah've 'ad enough, ah can't tek anymore! The hysteria in her voice frightened me. Ah'm gunner throw meself over t' waterfall!" She flung the door open and stumbled out.

"Look wat yer've done now yer silly little buggers," snapped Mammy. "Mi mother told yer t'stop rowing." Realising it was all our fault, I began to wimper. Arnold chased after Mammy and I dashed after them.

Weak and no doubt feeling dizzy Nanna had collapsed on the top of the steps that led to the 'owd 'ouse. There she sat with her shawl flapping around her, and head in her hands sobbing. Mammy, for the first time I could remember, had her arm around Nanna and was trying to comfort her. "Cum on Mother," she said soothingly "Yer can't stop h'out 'ere – yer'll catch yer death o' cold," Nanna's cries flung out like rooks released from the 'owd 'ouse

"Ah'm gunner stop 'ere till ah die," she wept, rocking backwards and forwards as though in pain.

For long enough, Arnold and I didn't know what to do, and stood shivering on the steps, leaving Mammy to whisper stuff to Nanna. After the moans stopped, Nanna's back looked like a sack hunched over, all lifeless. Arnold and me looked at each other, then, him first, we slipped past Mammy who was huddled over Nanna, and ran down the steps. Nanna's old face was the same tired shade as my thin socks, and made worse still by the streaky tears and the gas lamp. Her lips were turning blue. Our Kathleen had looked like that the last time I saw her.

"Don't cry Nanna." I pleaded. "We'll never fratch agen ah promise." Tears pricked the back of my eyes. I wound my arm around her neck and begged her to go in, but it was no use. Nanna was lost.

Arnold's worried little voice wobbled like a wonky saw as he tried to console her too. "We'll never fall out agen, Nanna," he promised." An' if ah tell a lie yer can spit in me eye." Nanna ignored him...

After a while, we all fell silent, and Mammy went to fetch the itchy blanket to cover Nanna up, whispering kind words to her every now and then, and shivering before falling silent again. Eventually she said to us, "Yer'd best get in before yer catch yer deaths hu'double pneumonia." But I couldn't go and warm myself and leave poor Nanna in the cold when I was to blame. Arnold must have thought the same for he stayed put, hands in pockets. If Nanna were to freeze to death in the night, we'd all die with her.

Over the valley electric lights from happier homes blinked across at us. The occupants no doubt sitting in an easy chair listening to the wireless; or busy in the kitchen making tea and toast. Maybe one day life might be like that for us. Every now and then beams of light from passing cars lit Nanna's back as they passed. But we were still alone with our problem.

If only Graham would come home. He could sort this mess out, although Mammy had done her best. We were all relieved when just before midnight, the familiar clump of his footsteps could be heard, and Mammy cocked her head and said, "It's h'our Graham." We ran to meet him, all three of us, leaping around him with anxious words.

"'Ang on... 'ang on a minute," he pushed us off. "'Ah can't 'ear a word any on yer's sayin'. Shut up, you two, n' let yer Mother speak."

"They were fratchin' h'over a pram er summet," Mammy trembled. "Ah told em t'stop it but they wouldn't. Next thing ah knew me Mother were out o' bed n' threatening t'commit suicide. She's been sitting on t'steps h'ever since."

Graham looked horrified and threw up his hands in despair.

"There's always summet!" he declared. "Always summet! If it in't one damn thing it's another. Ah'm bloody well fed up!"

I crumbled under his impatience. Perhaps he saw this and realising that all our hopes were pinned on him, began to speak a little more calmly.

"Oh, cum on then lets see what the bloody 'ell's 'appening. Wi' a bit o' luck she'll cum in fer me."

As he led the way through the suffocating darkness it was obvious Nanna hadn't moved since we'd left her. She was sitting stiff like a mound of earth that had been dumped there, and froze hard in the night. Graham approached quietly. The damp, earthiness of the December evening was suddenly invaded by the smell of mothballs from Graham's blazer. Sitting down on the step beside Nanna, he said "Wat yer doin' out 'ere in t'cowd? Yer gunner get pneumonia. Cum on, let's get yer inside where it's warm."

Silence.

With his hand placed gently on her icy shoulder he quietly persisted. "Cum on let's get yer inside, you've been out 'ere long enough." Still no response. At this point Graham decided it might be a good idea to take her by the arm and lead her in. Mammy had already tried this, without success. Graham was met with the same reaction. Nanna sprang to life and fought him off like a tigress.

It didn't take him long to realise that there was no way Nanna was going to move until she was ready. "Look, it's no good us all sitting out 'ere freezing t'death," he said. "You two go in n' get t'bed."

Arnold and I objected. Graham insisted. "Wen she decides t'cum in ah'll waken yer up an' tell yer."

So with downcast steps the two of us trailed indoors. Mammy followed, a moment later. "Ah'll scald us a pot o' tea," she said. As Mammy fumbled around in the darkness looking for a candle, Arnold and I clambered, trembling, into bed. Arnold shook out the old army coat to share between us.

"Do yer think she'll die?" I whispered nervously.

"No, ah've already teld yer," Arnold was typically optimistic. "She's gunner be alright... you'll see, she'll cum in before long."

If she did die it would be all our fault.

The word love was never used in our house, but I knew that what I felt for Nanna was special. To be without her would be worse than loosing arms or legs

Eventually, worn out with all the worry we fell asleep. But rest was fitful. The two of us kept wakening each other up as we tossed and turned. Every time I woke, a feeling of despair swept its cold brush over me. Nanna still hadn't come in. And when she did come in, would she have caught her 'death o' cowd'? I prayed to Jesus.

Presumably Graham and Mammy had continued their vigil. They must have been like ice. It was cold enough indoors... but I dreaded to think what it might be like outside.

Just before daybreak, a commotion at the door woke us up again. Nanna was hobbling indoors aided by both Graham and Mammy. In a flash, Arnold and I were out of bed and pattering towards the little group in our bare feet.

"Sit down 'ere, mother," said Mammy as she guided our numb Nanna to a seat on the couch. Nanna stiffly sat. Through the pale morning I could see that the three of them were tired out, their faces pinched and grey.

I wanted to put my arms around Nanna, bury my head in her shawl and beg forgiveness, but I didn't dare. To upset her again would be too much to bear, and I didn't want her fingers to snap off like icicles if she moved them before they'd thawed.

❧❧

The next few weeks were a nightmare. Nanna became desperately ill but refused to have a doctor. "They'll tek children away," I heard her whisper to Graham when he dared to suggest it. Graham ummed and ahhed, and the doctor wasn't sent for.

We hadn't seen a feather of Mammy's tail since the morning that Nanna had come in. After making sure she was safely in bed Mammy had disappeared down the road and hadn't been seen since. It was left up to the three of us to nurse Nanna better. We'd begun by making her a pot of warm, sweet tea, which Graham had held up to her lips while she'd slowly sipped it. Her skeleton body had trembled as

67

Arnold filled the hot water bottle and placed it at her feet. After sitting outside for fourteen hours the rough blanket and greasy tickin must have felt like heaven.

Graham did his best to reassure me that Nanna wouldn't die, but one night when Nanna had had a particularly bad delirious attack, she'd insisted that little Kathleen had just walked over her bed. Her voice was feeble, her forehead damp. "Ah felt her feet run across t'blanket," she murmured. "She's cum t'tek me back with 'er."

I'd imagined a little figure dancing across the rough blanket. She was as I had seen her last in a blue flowered dress and red sandals, looking at Nanna and smiling. I had almost heard her giggle.

As our main priority now was to look after Nanna whilst Graham was at work, Arnold and I stayed off school. But our care was basic. We filled the stone hot water bottle and made sure she had a warm drink. Sometimes we made her a bowl of bread and milk, or a cup of arrowroot, fed to her in a little white invalid pot with a spout on. What Nanna really needed though were warm soups, stews and milk puddings. Graham also told us to rub a few drops of Camphorated Oil onto her chest. "It will 'elp t'clear 'er bronchial tubes," he said.

As December went on, we continued trying to look after Nanna. Although we were still drawing her pension and there was always the bit of money that Graham earned at the mill, food rations were low. Arnold and I thought we'd better take ourselves off shopping.

"Nanna might eat a bit of John West salmon," I said, shaking the few coins in my fist.

We ran down the Switchback, through Towngate to Johnson's at the bottom of Peel Street. Arthur Schofield who worked there, smiled as we went in. Hams hung up like chunky rounders bats covered in muslin, and the smell of coffee cheered us up no end. We squinted along the shelves at tins of Lin Can peas, Spam and Ideal Milk before spying the salmon.

"Shall we buy Nanna some of that?" Arnold, pointed to cough mixture. I suggested she might prefer some Angel Cake, and a big piece of cheese cut from the slab. We whispered in the corner where the ground coffee was, and tried to add on our fingers how much our shopping would come to.

"Maybe," thought Arnold, "If we didn't get everything, we'd 'ave enough to get some brandy wi' t'rest on t'way 'ome. That'd be better nuh silly owd medicine. What would Nanna like best?"

"Salmon n' Angel Cake," I said.

So we forgot about the cheese, and stopped off at the back door of The Junction instead, and handed over five shillings for a miniature bottle of Napoleon Brandy.

Arnold had also found a bottle of Carters's Little Liver Pills somewhere in the pantry. Thinking that these would do her good he'd tried, unsuccessfully, to make her swallow one.

By Christmas the situation had got worse. Not only had we run out of coal and electricity we had no shillings for the gas meter either. Whilst other children waited with eager excitement for Christmas morning we anticipated a bleak one. Nonetheless, I was absorbed by it. I would press my nose against the shop windows and dream. Walkie-talkie Dolls had just become popular. Patricia and Margaret had even written a letter to Father Christmas asking for one. Arnold and I had never believed in Father Christmas, but if he had have been real I would most certainly have asked for a doll with plaited hair and big blue eyes, with a printed dress that was pressed to perfection and even smart white shoes and socks. They came in a box from Russell's Toy Shop that was almost as big as me. On each box, big red letters told you that the doll could say 'Ma-ma'.

If I could only borrow the spark-man from my Rupert Bear Annual. With magic sparks from his Wishing Powder, anything was possible. All I had to do was wish. First of all I'd ask the spark-man to make Nanna well again. Then I'd ask if it were possible to have five pounds to spend on Christmassy things. I had it all worked out. Top of my list would be a Christmas tree from Moorhouse's, with a box of glass baubles (the ones with frosty bits on), a glittering fairy for the top and several strands of silver tinsel. My next stop would be the chemist. In their window I'd recently spotted a small piece of cardboard with tortoiseshell hair slides clipped onto it. One of these would make an ideal present for Nanna. On a shelf above were some little bottles of Eau de cologne, which I thought Mammy might like. Graham could have a white rayon shirt with a collar from the Co-op. (The one he wore for going out was a bit tattered.) Next, and probably the most exciting of all, would be choosing something for Arnold and me. As well as the Walkie-talkie doll I would also have liked two Annuals – Rupert Bear and Sooty; a Wilkinson's Sweetshop, a crayoning book, some new wax crayons, and a three-wheeler bike with a boot at the back.

I could see myself running on Carr's Road to Walkers, and gazing at the big wooden table at the back of the shop where they displayed piles of exciting toys. I could buy Arnold a big box of Meccano, for two pounds five shillings, and a tin plate toy like a fire engine. He would love these. I might even have enough money left from my magic five pounds to buy him a popgun.

Imagine waking up on Christmas morning to find this huge pile of presents beneath the tree, each gift wrapped in coloured paper. There would be a fire in the grate, candles on the tree, holly, crepe paper trimmings and balloons hanging from the beams like gleaming moons. The house would be as clean as Margaret Cotton's front room. Nanna would love that – she often told us how spotless she was in her younger days. In the pantry there would be lashings of food; pork pies, mince pies, luncheon meat, a box of chocolates with a ribbon and roses on the lid. Even a big block of butter straight from the barrel in the Co-op; a turkey, big as a bus; some rosy apples, tangerines, carrots, brussell sprouts and heaps of potatoes. A wonderful Christmas – just like the ones in my Rupert book.

Unfortunately, spark-men and wishing powder were only a figment of Alfred Bestall's[*] imagination. I awoke on Christmas morning to a miserable house with no tree, no trimmings and no presents. The threat of Nanna dying still hung over us. It hadn't even snowed.

I thought of rich Uncle Harold and Cousin Miriam sitting down at a white-clothed table just further down the road elegantly eating a feast with gleaming knives and forks. The food parcel, which had been delivered by his son-in-law two weeks earlier, had disappeared in quicksticks. We had devoured the pound of mixed biscuits almost immediately and because we had no idea how to go about

---

[*] *Author and illustrator of Rupert the Bear books.*

making a proper meal, food like 'Ye Olde Oak Ham', had been cut into thick chunks and eaten from the tin with our grubby hands. The jelly was equally flummoxing, so we broke it off the lump and ate it like sweets. Uncle Harold had also packed a Robertson's Christmas pudding into the bottom of the box. It looked delicious on the wrapper – a piping hot dessert with a sprig of holly sticking out of the top. Mrs Schofield said it had to be steamed for hours, but that was after we'd eaten it, cold, disappointing and a bit sickly, but definitely filling.

Arnold was up and about the same time as me. He had spent the night at the foot of Nanna's bed and I think I may have trodden on him as I clambered out. I hoped Nanna hadn't mistaken my footsteps for those of Kathleen's. Arnold was still wearing the same grubby clothes as he had worn for months, a soiled shirt, dirty pullover and filthy trousers. His unwashed hair was plastered to his head and as he slithered off the bed I could see that his thin, bare legs were covered in muck roaks and bruises.

"Is mi Nanna alright?" He asked me.

"Yeah, she's still breathin', ah can see 'er shawl movin' up n' down a bit."

Arnold checked for himself, then picked up a pair of muddy wellington boots and slipped them onto his bare feet.

"We'll light t'fire n' get t'kettle on before she wakens up then," he ordered "You go n' get some sticks n' ah'll see if there's some water in t'pot."

Buckling up my shoes, I grabbed a brown paper carrier bag and hurried outdoors. Everywhere seemed quiet and still as I ran down the steps, past the 'owd 'ouse and into the lane where the sticks were. Although, for us, the day would be no different than any other, it still felt special. Apart from the bleating of a few sheep and the odd sparrow chirping, there was no sound at all. It made me think of 'Away in a Manger' which I began to sing to myself as I unlatched the gate.

My first job was to look for some thin, dry sticks that would be suitable for lighting. Big, fat ones would only burn when the fire was already blazing. Thin sticks I snapped into small pieces and put in my bag, the larger ones I bundled together and carried under my arm. Newly fallen branches I left to season, and wet sticks were only gathered when desperate. This would not be my only stickin trip of the day. Wood burnt quickly and it would take more than one load to boil a kettle full of water.

Nanna had her eyes open when I got back but she was staring into space. As I wafted past the bed towards the fireplace I longed for a cheery smile and a word or two.

"'ave got watter ready," said Arnold, pointing towards the sooty copper kettle standing on the hearth. "'n 'ah've put some tea in t'pots – but we 'aven't much left so don't you go putting any more in. Last night Graham said we've t'make it last another two days.

Arnold had already raked out the ashes so all I had to do was lay a few sticks onto some crumpled paper and set them alight. Within minutes a fine blaze filled the grate. I lifted the kettle onto the old iron rib and Arnold busied himself by snapping big fat sticks into more manageable lengths.

Having got the fire going, my next job was to empty the slop bucket, which, depending on what was in it, either went down the drain or through the hole in the seat of the outside lavatory. Today it was the lavatory. This was precarious and I had to be careful if I wanted to arrive at my destination without having slopped half of the revolting contents down the back of my leg.

Wobbling down the pavement, I wondered if Pat and Margaret had received their dolls. I bet they had. Perhaps they'd let me play with them next time I called. I thought of Nutwood too and Rupert's cosy living room. With my mind full of these Christmassy thoughts, I heaved the bucket onto the wooden seat and began to tip whatever was in it down the hole. I tried not to think about the contents. They smelt horrible. It would have been sensible to swill the bucket out before taking it back. But no one had ever said that, so back it went with drops still dribbling from its rim.

Graham, who was making the most of not having to go into work, didn't get up until well gone ten. By this time Arnold and I had propped Nanna up and we were holding a cup of warm, weak tea up to her mouth. She sipped it slowly.

Graham filled a pan with water and told Arnold to fetch another bundle of sticks. "We'll boil them there sprouts," he said. Arnold and I got quite excited about our Christmas dinner. He made endless journeys down the lane stickin whilst I diddled around watching Graham put the dozen little green cabbages into the pan. Once on the rib we waited patiently for the sooty-bottomed pan to come to the boil. Arnold kept prodding the sprouts with a two-pronged fork to see if they were ready.

Half an hour later Graham took the pan off the rib and teemed the boiling water into the empty slop bucket. Nanna refused the sprouts but she did have few more sips of cold weak tea.

PART 4

CHAPTER TWELVE

NEW YEAR '58

By January, the mild weather had deserted us and the ground turned solid and silver. Stickin' was impossible, frost had glued the sticks down, and despite much poking and proding, they refused to budge. So, no electric, gas, coal or sticks. We must have found something though, at some point, Arnold and me, treading carefully down Private Road with old socks over our shoes to stop us sliding. Enough to boil some water to make Nanna a drink.

That week, roadmen came to mend a wall between Boat Lane and the Two Police. I noticed them on my way to fetch candles from Nellie Beardsall's, sitting outside their wriggly tin hut warming their hands over a burning brazier. They were still sitting there, this time laughing over steaming pots of tea when I passed, blue-kneed, on my way home.

They still had their hut and stove set up several days later. Arnold had been to talk to them, and apparently they'd let him have a warm, and given him a wedge of cake to eat.

"Will yer ever mend walls up 'ere agen?" he'd said, as they'd packed up their shovels and all their stuff into the back of their lorry and driven off past Uncle Harold's.

When our Graham passed on his way home from work that evening, he noticed a pile of coke left behind, near the trodden down patch where the hut had been.

"Ah'm goin' dahn in a bit t'get some of that there coyl," he told us.

Sure enough, after having a pot of tea and listening to the Archers, he grabbed the old ex-army coat from Nanna's bed, and stuffed a couple of carrier bags deep into the pockets.

"Ah won't be long." He turned up the collar of the coat and disappeared into the night.

The candle had burned down some by the time he burst back in, bags of coal like lumpy heads, under each arm. I ran to shut the door. He dumped each bag on the hearth, muttering "By 'eck, by 'eck," and shook out his arms and hands. "Reit let's get this fahr goin'," he stammered, his teeth clattering loudly against each other. "Arnold, pass that there paper."

Graham used the flame from the only candle lit, and touched it to the paper with trembling hands. But a bit of newspaper and coal were not enough to get the fire going properly, so Graham ripped strips of oilcloth up from the floor, and smashed a wooden chair to pieces and flung most of that on the fire too.

"Shall ah pull t'sideboard drawers t'bits an' all?" Cried Arnold, leaping to his feet.

"Don't be so bloody stupid," snapped Graham, blowing on his hands, and taking up the draw-tin. "Tell thee wat, stick sum watter in t'kettle ready."

I hopped about, pleased to have some warmth at last. "We're gunner have a fire, Nanna."

Nanna, propped up in bed, said nothing, just watched as Graham pulled away the draw-tin, revealing yellow flames.

"Ah thowt coppers were gunner nab me," muttered Graham when we'd finally settled around the blaze. He was plying candles to try and get another half hour's burning. "Police car slowed down as ah were passin' t'Motorman's Café. They must've thowt ah looked shifty wi t'bags under mi arms."

The coal was ours now though, and reflected back two suns in Graham's eyes as he shaped the warm lump of candle into a waxy thumb-end. "Fetch mi that bit o'band Arnold, will yer, fer t'wick."

Our fire blazed bright for most of the evening, but by the following dinner time was no more than grey ashes in a cold grate. When Miss Newton and Mr Bruce turned up, they shook their heads at the cheerless fireplace.

Arnold scowled and took off the moment he saw them, and Nanna just nodded her head and said no more. Mr Bruce muttered gruffly to Miss Newton, and strode into the kitchen to stab his pickaxe nose into our cupboards.

Tweedy Miss Newton smiled down at me, and commented on various things, but all the time her eyes wandered; from the ragpile, to the remaining pieces of coal and what was left of the chair back in the hearth, saved for a bit of fire tonight.

Bossy Bruce re-emerged, frowning, and running an impatient hand through grey, receding hair. "Same old story," he growled.

"Have you seen anything of the childrens' mother recently, Mrs Peace?" Miss Newton asked, approaching the bed.

"Not a-lately," Nanna wheezed.

They poked round a minute more, asked me a few more questions, and headed for the door. Mr Bruce went without even saying goodbye.

"Soon be spring," said Miss Newton, and with a flash of auburn hair and tweed, was gone, out into the winter.

But before spring, we had February to cope with. Each fifteen-minute trip to the well, brought back a bucket of water iced over on the surface during the walk back down the hill and across the road

Our milk fared slightly better considering we had further to go to fetch it, all the way up the cart track opposite the Shepherd's Boy, to Warhurst's smallholding. The billycan had a lid on, and its handle squeaked as I swung it.

And then the snow came, the worst for eleven years, according to Little Tommy who came up with his shovel to dig us out. Arnold and I ran outside to kick up snow in our wellington boots – his given to him by someone Graham knew, and flopping about all over the place, mine tight on my feet, bought from a jumble sale two years ago.

I hobbled about, making foot prints as deep as tunnels, accidently putting one boot in a drift, and ending up thigh high in snow. Arnold wanged a snowball at me which I knew nothing about till it clouted me on the cheek.

"Arnold!" I scolded. "Yer could've 'ad mi eye out."

Arnold laughed and jumped about, then slipped right over and disappeared into the high, white road. He didn't come up again.

"Arnie," I called, cautiously stepping towards the cold, ragged crater where he'd vanished. "Arnie, will yer ever walk agen?"

Surely, if he couldn't, he'd be taken away.

Arnold said nothing. I peered over the huge snowhole, my brother was a star sprawled face up at the bottom, spattered with snow which had landed on him when he'd fallen. Snowflakes tiptoed out of the grey sky and settled on his thin clothes and pale pixie face, he didn't even look alive.

"Arnold!" I shrieked.

Suddenly, the ghostly mound reared up with a mighty roar, showering snow everywhere. It was like the frightful pictures Graham said played at Marsden Bug 'ole. I screamed.

The apparition laughed, and shook the snow out of his hair.

"Ha ha, got yer." Arnold brushed down his sleeves. Snow fell off in flurries.

"That wasn't funny. Ah though yer'd broken yer legs, or summet."

"You've got a big red mark where that snowball 'it yer," grinned Arnold.

With a hand gloved in an old sock, I touched the side of my face, it still stung. It was the only bit of feeling I had left up there.

The snow feathered down all day, and carried on into the night. By the next day, the mess we'd made down Private Road had been blotted out, and was like a big white sheet of paper again. The tips of fence posts barely poked above the surface, and branches hung heavy under the weight of snow. I struggled across Manchester Road with the water bucket. Not sure if I'd make it back alive, I gritted my teeth against the cold, and the sore, scarlet wellington scars round my calves.

Arnold wanted to make a sledge. He'd nakkled one up last winter but sold it to a boy he knew, intending to save up for a Davy Crockett outfit, but buying a slab of McGowens toffee and two ounces of Kali instead. He disappeared into the 'owd 'ouse. If he was staying off school again, so was I. Besides, I'd never have made it into the village.

Graham had managed to get into work though, and came tramping home again at teatime, stamping the snow off his wellington boots on the step, and shutting the door quick before too many flakes blew in. He'd brought back an Examiner he'd been given by one of the foremen and read bits out very slowly between mouthfuls of weak tea.

"'Vehicles snowed up,'" it seys, 'villages isolated. Huddersfield and district was today still reeling from the onslaught of its heaviest snow blizzard since 1947 – and the weather forecast this morning produced the likelihood of still more snow showers.'" He looked up at Nanna, cradling a warm pot between thin fingers, and continued "'Several outlying villages are completely cut off by snowdrifts, some of which are up to 6 feet in depth, and while bus services had been resumed to many parts this morning it was practically impossible in the majority of cases to maintain a regular timetable.'"

"I 'aven't seen th'up bus for days," I shivered, glancing over Graham's shoulder at a picture of a car abandoned overnight in Princess Street in town, and a pile of traffic snowed up in Northgate.

"Look at yond poor bugger," Graham wagged his finger at a third picture of a man trying to dig out his van. "It goes on to say that the post's been disrupted, Standedge has been closed, folk 'ave collapsed an' deed[*] an' 'Yorkshire is littered with abandoned vehicles.'"

"It's not all bad news though," I pointed to other headlines on the same page. "Sir Winston is 'very well' and the Queen Mother's in Australia. Will she 'ave been snowed in?"

"Uw dun't know t'meanin' u't word," scowled Graham "This paper'll leet tomorrers fahr if ah can scrat up some lumps er coyl out of these ashes." He folded the Examiner and tipped the last of his tea into his mouth.

---

[*] *Died.*

CHAPTER THIRTEEN

APRIL '58

Mammy left Topczewski, and not before time. She moved into a little house up Hard End, and told me all about it one day when I'd happened to bump into her in Nellies.

"Why don't yer cum an' stay wi' me a bit," she asked, picking up a bottle of Stardrops.[*]

"Yer, alright." I replied, without thinking why I'd said it. We made arrangements, and I left with my parcel of candles.

On Sunday, I went, taking a couple of annuals and a small ball. Mammy made me welcome.

"Sit yer down." She pointed to a chair at the table under the window. "H'al scald a pot er tea."

Mammy's new house was much like her house in Towngate but without the wine bottles. Just as small and neat, and smelling of Wimsole.

It wasn't the same walking down Mount Road to school in the morning, and I got to wondering how Nanna would be doing without me. I went up Standedge to visit her after school.

"There's a sink in an alcove, an' oilcloth, an' a square of carpet in th'ouse. And she's got red an' black wallpaper," I told Nanna when she asked about the house. It felt funny to walk back towards Marsden in the twilight, and climb up Mount Road, to spend the night at Mammy's.

She was in a good mood all week, and filled me up with arrowroot biscuits and iced buns. On Friday night I went to bed planning to go stickin' for Nanna in the morning, in case Arnold hadn't got enough.

I was woken suddenly, prodded and shaken. Mammy was wild; hair like shabby crow feathers, eyes unblinking.

"Someone's h'in t'cellar," she shrieked "h'ave 'eard 'em!"

I was sitting up before my eyes had ajusted to the dark. I'd come up too quick and felt wuzzy for a minute. Then Mammy's words sank in.

Someone's in the cellar.

I listened, but nothing. Mammy hopped to the bedroom door, stooped to

---

[*] *Disinfectant made at Thorton & Ross in Linthwaite.*

listen. All I heard was my own heart duh dumming, and blood swishing in my ears. Mammy flew back and perched on the bed-edge with me. Through the gloom I could see the whites of her eyes.

She argued with herself whether it would be better to run out and get the poker or a big pan and lie in wait at the top of the cellar steps.

"Ah'll knife 'em, ah will. Ah'll bloody well knife 'em," she whispered.

I strained my ears for the intruder. Next, Mammy suggested running for a policeman. But we stayed on the edge of the bed, digging our nails into the blankets

Maybe it was Topczewski prowling about drunk, after Mammy. Happen he'd come to murder her for leaving him. When he saw me he'd probably kill me too. He hadn't managed to shove me up the chimney when I was younger, this time he wouldn't want to fail. The memory of blood in the snow oozed back and I imagined his shadow creeping up the cellar steps, a dark mill chimney topped with a trilby, and pushing open the bedroom door, glaring at us with his stone face. I wanted to climb out of the bedroom window, and jump out, and run all the way back to Nanna's. Why had I ever thought it was safe at Mammy's? But I stayed on the bed listening to the rasps of her breathing. She picked up a brass candlestick and held it ready. We were still like that when grey morning leaked through the curtains.

The lighter it got, the safer we felt. Mammy went down.

"It's h'all right," she said, but if it had been Topczewski he might return tonight. I was going to take no chances. Forgetting books and ball, I took a different route over the moor, and was back at Nanna's just before nine, this time for good.

❧❦

"That bloody woman! She's gunner 'ave us talk er Marsden agen!" Graham had just arrived home from work and his face was as black as March Hill. "Read that," he growled, thrusting the front page of The Huddersfield Examiner in front of me. He was pointing to a big bold headline.

'CHILDREN HAD TO FEND FOR THEMSELVES.'

"Read it!" He demanded again. "Read it out loud!"

He was shouting so fiercely that I didn't dare defy him.

"'Whilst their eighty-year-old grandmother was ill in bed,'" I began, "'two children, a boy aged eleven and his eight-year-old sister, lived in the house where there was little food and no coal...'" It was like the black text had jumped off the page and slapped me in the face. "'...and had to fend for themselves.'" I stuttered.

"Go on!" yelled Graham.

"'This was stated at Huddersfield West Riding Court today when the children's mother, Kathleen Topczewski of 2 Bridge End, Marsden, was before the court for failing to send the children to school regularly and was fined £1 in each case. The magistrates also granted an application by Mr. Alan Carter, Education Welfare Officer, to have the children brought before the Juvenile Court.

"'Defendant pleaded guilty to failing to send the girl to school and not guilty to failing to send the boy.'"

'92 OUT OF 100'

"'Mr. Carter said that between November 25, 1957 and February 21, 1958, the boy had been absent ninety-two times out of possible attendance of 100. The girl had attended on thirty-one occasions out of a possible 100.

"'Mr. Carter said that during this period defendant lived with her husband at 2, Bridge End, Marsden. The children, of her former marriage, lived with their eighty-year-old grandmother at Millstone Cottages, Marsden.

"'The grandmother had looked after the children for the past two or three years in spite of her age and the fact that she was not in good health.

During a large part of the time when the children had been away from school the grandmother had been seriously ill in bed.

"'The children had to fend for themselves. There was little food and no coal in the house.'"

'WOULD NOT HAVE THEM.'

"'Defendant had said that her husband would not have the children in the house. When asked if she provided money for them defendant had said that money should come from a maintenance order made against her previous husband.

"'In court defendant said that she wanted the children with her in her own home. However, she said that she had to work. Her previous husband had not always paid the maintenance. She alleged.

"Give me one more chance and I will see that they go to school, she said…'"

Although I had stumbled over quite a lot of the words and didn't quite understand the meaning of most of it, I got the general idea. Mammy had been 'adup' for not looking after us properly. Not only that, Arnold and I had to appear in court!

Nanna shook her head and said "What's ever's gunner 'appen next?"

That night I decided the best thing to do was to arrive in Marsden early. That way I could meet my friends in dribs and drabs rather than in one large group.

As soon as I heard the mill hooter go at a quarter to seven I was out of bed and washing my hands and face in a bowl of cold water. Graham had already left. He liked to arrive at the mill early so that he could kreall the bobbins.[*] He didn't like running the risk of being late either. Latecomers were locked out and missed a full days pay.

It was just turning light as I arrived in the village; one or two mill workers were making their way to Bank Bottom, Bruce's and the Belgi Firm. I hung about by the river and in order to pass time picked up a few pebbles, threw them into the dark water below, and watched them land with a loud plop.

Suddenly, wearing a pair of men's heavy denim jeans and some old boots clomped Mammy. The greasy smell of mill oil clomped with her. I couldn't pretend not to see her.

"Wat you doin' ere so early?" She asked.

"Dunno," I lied. "Ah just set off sooner n' normal."

There was an awkward silence. I slung a few more stones into the river. She didn't mention the newspaper report and I certainly wasn't going to. But she did ask me to meet her in the mill canteen at dinnertime. "Ah'll buy yer yer dinner," she said. (She'd been working at Bankbottom as a Fettler[**] for the last three weeks.) I didn't particularly want her to buy me my dinner, but decided that if I were to refuse she would be very hurt.

"Be there fer about 'arf twelve."

Waterside

---

[*] *Exchanging the empty bobbins all along the length of the mule gate for full ones. Each bobbin was five feet long and wound soft yarn into hard-spun yarn.*

[**] *A fettler cleans the straps and chains of the scribbler (see 'Feeder' chapter. 4) and carding machines, removing excessive grease and mucky fibres with a fettling comb.*

After she had gone I made my way towards Market Place hoping I would bump into Patricia Blackburn. She lived up Oliver Lane just across from the Co-op. Before long Patricia came trotting round the corner by Russell's Toy Shop. If she mentions owt about it, I thought, I'll say it couldn't have been Mammy – her name's Wainwright.

I would have given anything to swap places with Patricia. She didn't seem to have a care in the world. Her freckled face shone and her sandy waves were held in place by neat ribbons as she hopped and skipped towards me. She was chattering about Lenny the Lion that she'd watched on television the night before and said nothing of the report.

No one else mentioned the report either – not even the teachers. It was like our shameful little secret. But I still had to face Mammy in the mill canteen!

At twenty five past twelve I made my way along Fall Lane and into the little stone building where the mill workers ate. Most were lined up by the counter buying their dinner; some were seated at big square tables already tucking in. Others were just ambling along. Mammy was already standing in the queue.

"Ooo – oo!." She hooted as I walked through the door. The noise of it turned heads.

We ate dinner, and headed off to the toilet. On our way out, Mammy suddenly screamed at the half-dozen startled women in there washing their hands.

"What yer f------ starin' at. I 'eard yer whisperin'. Ah'll knife lot er yer, ah will, ah'll knife bloody lot er yer."

The women, shocked into silence, had probably been whispering about the questionable state of my velvet jumble sale frock with the dipping hem. But Mammy was screeching and squawking about the report. I thought the only way to distract her was to tug at her fluzzy sleeve.

"Ah don't want t'be late fer school, Mammy," I said.

❧❧

Eventually, we were sent word that a date had been set for Arnold and me to go to court. Arnold was defiant about being 'adup, and kept saying "Ah'm goin' t'stay at 'ome an' look after mi Nanna", which probably meant that he was going to fix his 'erry cart, make a kite, or have a poke around Flint's barn instead.

Only when Mrs Reed[*] arrived to take us (No-one had seen Mammy since the canteen incident six weeks ago!) did Arnold realise that he had to go.

I had tried to make an effort to look tidy by smoothing down the front of my

---

[*] *Mr and Mrs Reed moved in next door after the people with the baby and the wireless left.*

frock, and putting on the cleanest pair of mucky socks I could find. Mrs Reed pecked about Arnold, who hadn't even tried.

"Roll yer shirtsleeves down, Arnold. You'll look a bit more respectable. And has your Graham got owt you can flatten this hair down with?"

Mrs Reed sighed when she saw him, rumpled sleeves zigging down his arms like the real zags on his sleeveless pullover. His frayed shirt collar waved hello to all the creases, and his hair looked different, all flat and slick with Brylcreem. But he had to do.

"Cum on then, get yer coats on," Mrs Reed shook her head, smiling.

Arnold hadn't a coat, but I put my blue gaberdine on, and all three of us set off for the bus. I sat straighter than a post all the way, rocking with the bus, and letting the corners pull me with them. At about this time I could have been anywhere on the moor, or throwing stones and bits of grass over Eastergate bridge into the stream, or even at school doing sums.

"Don't worry 'eather," Mrs Reed smiled, "we'll be home before you know it." I shrank instinctively away from her comforting arm, though I didn't really want to.

It felt like I'd swallowed hula hoops as we walked into the Juvenile Court in Huddersfield, and by the time we were sitting on the front bench in the large wooden room, they were twirling good. Even Arnold had stopped his defiant chatter.

The magistrates had bits of rag sewn on where their mouths should have been, and looked more fearful than Nutwood's schoolmaster chimp at his crossest. In fact, they looked sterner than Bossy Bruce who'd made us come in the first place. I found myself glancing around the vast, varnished prison for pointy dunce hats and hoping they'd make me stand in the corner nearest the door and freedom, where I might not hear them shout so loud at us, but Mrs Reed would surely not allow that.

We were ordered to stand when spoken to, before all the magistrates glaring down from their gallery. I almost expected flashes of lightning, like I'd seen on Patricia Blackburn's television set, when a monstrous man with a beard big enough to climb up, had boomed, "So mortal, you dare to defy the wrath of the Gods", nearly blowing away a tiny, little man with the wind from his words.

But there was no lightning as the voice called, "Are you Heather Wainwright?"

I nodded, wondering how long it might be before we'd be led away and locked up.

"And are you Arnold Haigh Wainwright?" the owner of the voice peered over the bench above us, and I could see the distorted reflection of the window in each eye of his spectacles.

"Yes," mumbled my brother, a tremble in his voice.

"And do you both realise the importance of attending school regularly?"

"Yes," we murmured together, but thought otherwise.

The crows chuntered to themselves in their nest while I looked round the middle of Mrs Reed's green two-piece, to whisper to Arnold, but he was staring to some invisible spot way down past his scuffed shoes.

The chuntering stopped.

"Are you the childrens' mother?" Mrs Reed was asked.

"No," she replied, and went on to explain herself before they all set up a-chuntering again, and fiddled with fountain pens, ajusted glasses and scraped their chins.

My fingers crawled into my mouth to be chewed, while a verdict was decided, and a sentence reached. We'd sometimes played gaolers at school – YOU WILL HANG BY THE NECK TILL YOU ARE DEAD – We'd even wrapped Martin Brown up in the swing chain till the bell went. But it didn't seem funny now.

"Thank you," echoed the voice from above. "You may leave."

By the time we got outside, it was raining.

As soon as we got back home, Arnold went to change into one of Graham's old boiler suits, and ran, flapping, to the 'owd 'ouse to help Graham do some nakklin', rolling up the wrists and ankles as he went. I followed, with my ball.

"'ow do," smiled Graham, and sat back on an old box, plucking up a cracked pot with his greasy hand. "Yond court wark ovver then?"

Arnold launched into an account of as many details as he could remember, with a sprinkling of new ones as well. I let him talk, and chucked my ball against the wall. Arnold leant in the door 'oyle, chuntering on. Graham supped his tea. Private Road shimmered with drizzle, and everywhere smelt warm and earthy, almost like summer.

Just then, footsteps and laughing made us look round. Arnold stopped mid-sentence. Two girls, about Graham's age, or maybe younger were coming up Private Road, their high heels grating on the loose stones. Arnold dropped the oily rag he'd been twisting about and started smoothing himself down.

"Is mi 'air alright, 'eather?" He whispered, staring at the girls as they clattered past, giggling. They never gave us a second glance, and disappeared onto Manchester Road. Arnold ran part way as they went. I returned to my ball, noticing Graham smile and shake his head, and drain off the last dregs from his pot.

One day, near the anniversary of Kathleen's death, Nanna decided she would like to put a memorial in the Colne Valley Guardian. After looking through some old copies she asked me to cut one out and take it down to Russell's Toy Shop.

Mr Russell was some sort of agent for the newspaper and accepted my screwed up offering.

Heather Coupland

WAINWRIGHT –

In loving memory of a dear granddaughter who passed away 13th May 1954, aged 6 years.

Dear Lord, wilt Thou a message take
To one who dwells above,
Tell her how much I miss her
And give her all my love."

CHAPTER FOURTEEN

AUTUMN AND WINTER '58

- DEZ WILSON -

Arnold started his first term at Colne Valley High in Linthwaite. It was about six miles from Marsden, and, as it had just been built, was known as 'The New School'. Every morning 'Stott's Tours', a bus company from Oldham, picked up several children from outlying places and took them to school. Uniform was compulsory: Arnold needed a black blazer with a red ram on the badge of its top pocket, a blue shirt, grey pants and stripy tie. Arnold had none of these. On that first morning he set off in a shabby tweed suit (some posh kid's cast off Mammy had bought from a jumble sale), a pair of worn out shoes, a red and white striped tee-shirt and no tie.

He returned that night looking even more disheveled. Some of the older boys had bashed him up, so he said. His shirt was torn and two of the buttons from his secondhand suit had been ripped off. A few days later the same boys slung him through an open window on the ground floor. Both Nanna and Graham tried to convince Arnold it would be better if he learnt to stick up for himself, but Arnold was too skinny to tackle bigger boys.

After six weeks of bashings Arnold finally decided enough was enough - he was never going to go to school again. Instead he spent his time stickin, shopping and scratting around on Flint's tip. He was indistructable, he said. The school board man would never catch him, he said.

One day, when I had decided to skip school as well, Arnold came rushing into the house, red faced and puffing.

"Bloody 'ell, school board man's 'ere. Ah've just seen 'im cumin' up t'road. Ah'm gunner 'ide in t'bedroom. Wat ever yer do, don't tell 'im where ah am." He darted through the living room and into the kitchen. I could hear the clump of feet as he charged up the wooden stairs. There was a knock on the door and Mr Carter burst in.

"Where's Arnold?" He barged across the room.

Nanna, who had barely time to gather her thoughts together, stared blankly at him. I said nothing.

"I know he's here somewhere. I saw him come through the door." Without asking permission, Mr Carter ran through the kitchen, up the stairs and into Graham's room. I ran after him.

"You may as well come out Arnold," he shouted. "I know you're in here somewhere." He began searching under the bed and behind the door. But I knew where Arnold was - he was in the back bedroom. I'd seen the door move slightly as I hovered on the landing. Whilst Mr Carter continued his search, I tip-toed towards the door and whispered, "Arnold, Arnold, let me in, 'es in Graham's room looking under t'bed." I could just make out the squashed shape of Arnold's eye as it appeared through the tiniest crack of the back bedroom door. I nipped through to join him.

A moment later Mr Carter was braying on the door and demanding we open it. "I know you're in there so you might as well come out."

"'elp me t' 'old t'door," said Arnold, struggling to keep it shut. Together we pressed our weight against it as hard as we could. Then, with Arnold's foot wedged tight against the bottom, he said, "Wen I say now - let go!" He was puffing and blowing and going red in the face. With as much effort as he could muster he shouted, "NOW!"

We both moved swiftly aside, a startled Mr Carter tumbled into the bedroom, and Arnold scarpered.

Stunned by his sudden fall, Mr Carter took a second or two to regain his composure: but then, he was back on his feet and darting after him. Not wanting to miss out on all the fun, I darted off too. As I rounded the corner by the 'owd 'ouse I could see Arnold running like billy-o down Private Road and that Mr Carter, having flagged down a uniformed A.A. man on his motorcycle, and the waterboard man, also on a motorcycle, was running hell for leather behind him. I trotted after everyone, at a safe distance, where I had a good view of the bottom of the road, and the madcap chase which was now in progress. Arnold; whippetty, slippery and wick, bounded tirelessly over fallen coping stones down the grassy path, and past my Pink Purslane Patch. Mr Carter lumbered along on overweight, middle-aged legs, over a fat fists-shake away. Each short step seemed faster than it actually was. "Stop, you rascal," he shouted at intervals. Next was the lanky A.A. man, helmet wedged like a burdensome second head beneath his arm, chopping up grass as he loped, with heavy, black boots. Each stride appearing to go further than it did. And then went the water board man, hampered somewhat by his long leather coat and struggling to remove his goggles with clumsy, gauntletted hands.

Where the path sloped down to the stream, it became more rocky and slippy. Here Arnold had the advantage. He was not at all bothered about falling into the water whereas Mr Carter was more cautious. Sloshing straight through the stream, Arnold took flight over the fence, across the grass verge and onto the road.

Mr Carter had to admit defeat. There was no way he was going to humiliate himself by getting soaked. Instead he threw his hands in the air, bent double in order to catch his breath and muttered, "Stupid little fool. Doesn't he realise I'm only trying to help him?"... The A.A. man muttered, shrugged, and started back up the path, followed by the Waterboard man.

A few months later, a brown envelope arrived through our letterbox. Inside, an official letter stated quite clearly that Arnold and Mammy must appear in court. Arnold was being 'tried' again for failing to attend school.

On the morning of the case even Mammy must have realised the seriousness of the situation and came up to collect him. They were going to catch a trolley bus to the same Juvenile Court we'd been to last spring.

When Mammy came home, she said Arnold had been made to wait in a dark corridor for what seemed absolutely ages before being taken into the courtroom and 'brought before the bench'. Like a convicted criminal he'd been asked to confirm his name and where he was from. The judge had then informed him he was being put on a 'full care order' and that he was going to live in a Children's

Home. According to the judge it was in Arnold's best interest. A welfare worker, whom he had never met before, led him out of the courthouse and into a car. There was only a time for a quick farewell to Mammy before leaving.

CHAPTER FIFTEEN

SUMMER '59

Saturday afternoons were a good time to sneak round Marsden on my own. For most of the shops, it was half-day shutting and I felt like I owned the village when no-one else was there, just like the park sometimes. Poking about in door'oyls, and crouching behind walls hiding from bandits was best when there was nobody to bother me.

Better still was when I pretended Indians had raided Marsden and taken everyone away (except Nanna who'd been allowed to move into Uncle Harold's house, and Graham and Arnold who'd gone with her, and several of my favourite friends and neighbours – and of course Mammy who had refused to be captured, and clobbered several indians with our chip pan.) and I could wander as I pleased through deserted shops, houses and streets.

What topped it all though, was when I had a bit of money in my pocket like I had one week. I nipped into Meakins on Brougham Road before it closed for the afternoon and bought a bow and arrow. Now I could be the best outlaw that ever lived. I scampered towards the Greenwood of Private Road, hiding behind trees and dodging the Sheriff of Nottingham. My gaberdine had to do for Lincoln Green and I shoved a discarded magpie feather behind my ear.

Then the thought occurred to me to go tatchin'.[*] I ran up home, grabbed a box of matches and ran out again, across Manchester Road and onto the moor. Just below my aeroplane, I crouched down, dropped my bow and arrow and started to light patches of grass. It wasn't such a warm day, but it hadn't rained since the last time Graham had set off to Wetherby on a bike ride with Barry Carter, and that was a bit ago.

The grass lit straight away, in several places which quickly became one big place. Tiny plumes of flame crackled louder than new paper bags, and wisps of smoke soon billowed up like rainclouds over Marsden Moor. A mouth of burnt brown spread before my eyes, hungry for more grass. Not satisfied with the bit it had, it gnawed more, till there was a huge golden circle burning and growing.

And it had to be stopped. I beat at it with my gaberdine, furiously, desperately. If the fire got bigger, I'd have no chance. Someone would ring the police and I'd be 'teken away'. This whole side of the moor would burn, Willie Woodward's goats tied to their stakes, all the sheep, and me along with them. I beat harder, smoke watering my eyes. Thump thump with my gaberdine. Some of the flames I stamped out. Thump thump echoed my heart. Just as one patch went out, another would still be spreading.

'Flap, stamp, flap, stamp.'

And finally it was all over. My throat felt tight and chokey. An area half the size of our kitchen smouldered, and I flopped down next to it, my chest hurting. I'd forgotten all about Robin Hood till I noticed my bow on the bronzed edge of frazzled grass. I picked it up, the green and red twists of string had almost burnt away, and the wood was scorched.

I trudged back down the hill and slunk in, dragging my smoky coat behind me, like a black sheep's tail.

---

[*] *Setting fire to dry grass.*

While poking about Marsden shops, I noticed something in Russell's window which was nearly as good as a norse, certainly as beautiful. A sky blue scooter which had TRIANG written on the side in daffodil yellow, and a price with lots of numbers in at the side.

"Buy me, buy me," it whispered.

Maybe if I lived in Nutwood.

I ran home to tell Nanna.

"Well love," she wheezed, between bites of lard-bread, "if ah cud afford to buy it yer, ah would, but it's a lot er money is nineteen shillin' nine an' elevenp'nce. Ah just 'aven't it."

Arnold had had many adventurous schemes, to make a bit of brass; from his 'en 'ut, to his push bike, and all the bits of nakklin' stuff he'd drag back from Marsden on his 'erry cart, and disappear with into the 'owd 'ouse. I felt it was time I did something of my own to help. It would take a bit to save up for a norse and that scooter, and before that we needed food in the house. I sat on our front steps resting my chin on my drawn up knees, waiting for a plan. When one came, it was brilliant.

So scraping up what change I could find, I dashed down to Marsden to buy half a dozen tiny calendars. I could cut out pictures from my comics, stick them onto the ripped off sides and flaps from cardboard boxes, and attach a calendar at the bottom. Folk would pay me good money for one of them. I made two that evening before the light faded.

The morning after, I met Jill. She was new in our class. Her family had just moved into a little place at Intake Head, further down the road than Millstone Cottages. At playtime, when we were standing on the swings and trying not to fall off, I told her about my calendars.

"Ah've made a norse an' cart, and a rabbit."

"I've got a rabbit," cried Jill. "Why don't you come round tonight and see him."

I went to Jill's a few times after that.

Calendar production ceased for a couple of days due to the lack of boxes. While I was kicking up my heels round the back of the house, Graham turned up with a present for me.

"Ah thowt yer'd like this," he grinned, handing me a crumpled pound note. "To get that scooter yer've been natterin about. Just you be careful wi' it, it's a lot of brass. Na then," he turned to go inside, "Ah bet there in't a reit lot in fer tea."

I flew straight down to Russell's, my hand folded round that magic money, and felt like the most important person in the world as I took away my new blue Triang.

It was a little bit small for me, but what did that matter. I whizzed down the pavement, up the canal bank and home.

After that evening, I scooted first to the waterfall, then down again as far as Marsden. On the Saturday Graham went to Malcolm's and brought a cardboard box back with him. I returned to work, cutting and sticking. I was very busy when the insurance man came by. He wore grey flannels and a crisp blue blazer, and had a side parting straighter than the canal.

"And what are you up to?" He asked, stepping over comics and bits of box.

"Mekin' calendars," I announced, "An' ah'm gunner sell 'em."

"I see, I see," replied the insurance man.

Later that afternoon, I scooted down Manchester Road, then up the lane to Jill's. She'd promised me I could help clean out the rabbit. I was just about home again when a policecar pulled up, and a head popped out and looked at me. Was something up? Was I not allowed to be riding a scooter which was too small for me?

"Are you Heather?"

I nodded.

"We're just going to your house. Is anyone in?"

"Mi Nanna, " I muttered. "She's in bed."

I left my scooter at the bottom of the steps, the policemen followed me in. They glanced at all my calendar stuff which carpeted the floor near the bed where I'd been working, then to my surprise, one of them asked Nanna if he could see a shopping list. I froze. If he found out that we had hardly any food in, he might send me off to a home, like Arnold, away from Graham and Nanna. I glanced at Nanna, propped up in bed, half asleep.

"What's Kitty been telling yer now!" She yawned.

The policemen looked blank. "There'll be one somewhere." Nanna shook her head. "Look over there, 'eather, and over there in t'cupboard."

I hunted around and eventually spotted one sticking out of one of my cardigan pockets in the ragpile. It was several months old. I handed it to the policeman.

"Boiled ham, bread, Typhoo Tea, sterilised milk, jam," he read, and nodded. We had obviously been well off that week. The policemen left as swiftly as they had come. I knew this had nothing to do with Mammy this time. It was that bloomin' insurance man.

The day school broke up for the six-week holiday I decided to go to Jill's on my scooter.

"We're off for a picnic," chirped Jill when she opened the door. "D'yer want t'come?"

So I scooted back down the lane and up Manchester Road, the sun burning the left side of my face, to prepare a picnic tea of my own. I burst into the house, gasping out my plan to Nanna on my way to the kitchen. What could I make? There was the Turog. Near it, some jam. The bread knife nearly sliced through my finger in my haste to carve out a wedge. I slopped jam onto it, carelessly folded it, squashed it down, and ran out, knocking the jam lid onto the floor, and leaving crumbs everywhere.

I climbed up onto my aeroplane[*] to wait for Jill and her family to pass by. The large sky melted into the brown moors opposite, like jam bleeding out of the edge of my sandwich into my palm.

It wasn't long before I spied them out, two small figures and a basket, with the smaller figure of Jill's little brother poddling just behind them. I ran to join them and we trotted off to Eastergate with our teas.

---

[*] *A boulder just above the well, which looked like an aeroplane body with stubby wings.*

Jill's mum had packed their wicker basket with shiny apples and soft neat sandwiches. Fairy cakes frilled out of a bag, and were taken out and laid in a circle on a plate. Jill's mum shook out a tablecloth and spread it on the uneven ground. Checked pillows of air sank slowly as the cloth settled. I clutched my jam-bread.

"Would you like one of these, Heather?" Jill's mum held out a meatpaste sandwich on a plate, but I was satisfied with what I had, and was just content to dabble my feet in the golden scaled water with everyone else, rinse my sticky hands and rub them dry down my frock.

Jill and her family moved that autumn to Holt Head in Slaithwaite, and took their rabbit with them. I rode up to Intake Head on my scooter after they'd gone, and peered through the empty window. I wondered how it might be if I returned to Millstone Cottages sometime, and there was no ragpile there. No battered armchair, no crackly wireless, no Nanna. I pushed my scooter home.

But it wasn't all bad. Arrangements had been made for me to visit Jill in her new house. I travelled up on the bus and spent the day playing in the lane, and exploring the fields.

Around four-thirty, I thought it was time to be getting back. I didn't really want to go, because I knew I probably wouldn't see Jill again. She'd be going to another school and making new friends. I'd have been all right here till morning, I could have curled up in a chair and only had a slice of bread for supper. But Nanna would worry, so Jill asked her mum about the buses. I'd have to catch one into Slaithwaite first, which were every two hours, then one to Marsden every other hour – and I'd just missed that.

Jill walked me to the bus stop, and despite the weather, I shivered. I was sorry to leave Jill. But the shivering didn't stop. It must have all been inside me, because Jill didn't seem to notice, and chattered about this and that. Her voice was distant, like I was inside Pule quarry and she was out in the sun, talking to me.

When the fence no longer felt like it would hold me up, I flopped onto the grass verge, and felt its velvet dryness on my legs. It was a huge pillow, the most comfortable bed ever, the only thing to stop me slipping down onto roadside gravel. It was an effort to get up out of all that softness when I heard the faraway voice of Jill saying the bus was coming.

I staggered onto it, muttering a goodbye in a voice which wasn't mine and paid my thrupence. No sooner had I collapsed onto the nearest black and red plush seat, I was in Slaithwaite and had to drag myself off again and wait an hour for th'up bus.

Don't Cry Nanna

I stumbled down Varley Road to the Marsden bus stop, and leaned on a post, holding my head. A few clouds came and went. No chance of sinking down onto one of those . To keep busy, and try and forget how I was feeling I started counting the bricks on a house opposite, but by the time I'd reached fifteen my eyes hurt too much and my brain switched off. The next brick changed form and became alive with sparkles, it heaved inward, then out as if the entire wall were breathing. I couldn't remember what number came after fifteen, and suddenly the whole wall fell away, crumbling into twinkly sand. Steadying myself against the post, I shook my head and the wall was back, solid and upright.

I'd given up all hope of th'up bus turning up, but then I saw it float round the corner, its shiny radiator grille grinning at me. "Thank you. Thank you for comin'." I wanted to say, but as usual got on in silence.

Back at home, nothing was as it should have been. Nanna was in bed, of course, but the shapes of the furniture seemed odd, a bit like that wall in Slaithwaite. It was as if I could see straight through everything. Or if I reached out to something that was within touching distance, it would suddenly be very far away. I'd had dreams like that.

I fell down onto the hard horsehair couch and closed my eyes. When they opened again, it was dark and I was shivering. There was no fire, no blankets around, no noise which sounded normal, just a horrible hissing in my head. It was impossible to move, everything hurt too much and I just didn't have the strength. So I stayed put, and shivered through the night.

There was a strange cockerel on the wall. I didn't remember having seen it before – or maybe I'd forgotten. Suddenly it wasn't on the wall, but there in front of my face, almost blinding me with its gaudy feathers. Then tiny on the wall again. Then so close I wanted to back away. It came and went with each pound of my head, trapping me on the horsehair couch. At last I pretended not to see it, maybe if it stayed small my head would stop hurting.

Black became smeared with grey, and shapes and edges slowly reappeared. Somewhere far away I thought I heard a cock crow, but I wasn't sure. Lights flashed past the curtains, and there were other sounds, but I couldn't move. Then it was light, and Graham was coming from the kitchen, then he was fettling something, then moving around doing something else. At one time, when the room was full of black and yellow candlelight, I heard low voices – Graham's and Nanna's, then the kettle whistling.

When it seemed I had no more sleep left in me, I tried stretching myself, and this time I moved. If I could just sit up for a while, and maybe say hello to Nanna, I might just feel better.

I managed to get into the kitchen and put the kettle on. While I was sitting down sipping my weak tea with Nanna, she said "Have yer been feelin' a bit any 'ow, love?"

"Ah'm alright now" I replied, between weakening thumps of headache, glad now that I had kept the whole truth from Nanna. Graham would have probably sent for the doctor, and the doctor might have suggested to Miss Newton that I'd be best 'teken away', like poor Arnie.

❧❧

Although I was quiet, I attracted friends like a merry-go-round, despite my grubbiness. Patricia Blackburn, my best friend, lived in the centre of Marsden with her mum and dad. I think she had a younger brother and sister, but I was too busy watching westerns on their black and white television set to notice. Patricia and I would sit glued to the Lone Ranger as he galloped across the screen on his silver steed – then just as he was about to capture a baddie – the picture would seesaw. A quick thump from Patricia would soon sort it out and the baddie would be hauled in – in one piece instead of a zigzag. For days I would be 'Hi-yo-o-o-o-o-Silverin' – it' around the playground, along the streets and down the alleyways, just knowing that when I grew up, I too was gunner 'ave a norse er mi own' – like the Lone Ranger.

I had a few grown up friends too like Mr and Mrs Sheard on Water's Road. They lived at the end of a beautiful little row of cottages near Eastergate. I first met them whilst zooming past their house on my new scooter.

Mr Sheard was busy in his waterside garden pruning his roses.

"Hello," he said as I scooted past. He sounded nice and looked friendly so I stopped to talk. Mrs Sheard, a plump little woman around seventy-five and about five feet tall popped her head round the door when she heard my voice. She had a warm, friendly face with nice hair that curled loosly around her head. Thick brown stockings covered her legs and on her feet she had a pair of sturdy lace-up shoes. She looked so much healthier than Nanna, and smarter, in a blue dress and wool cardigan.

"What's your name?" She asked.

"'eather."

"Heather. That's a nice name. Where do you live?"

Before long I found I was telling her all about Nanna, Graham and Arnold. She seemed very interested.

"Your Nanna's eighty! And she's looking after all of you!"

"Well, sometimes we look after 'er as well," I said.

"Yes, I'm sure you do," said Mr Sheard. You seem a very sensible little girl."

They went on to tell me they had just moved from York and that they had a little grandson called Malcolm.

"He's about the same age as you so next time he comes to stay you must come down and play," they said.

I went away feeling as bright as a buttercup.

From that day on, whenever they saw me passing their house, one of them would shout me across and invite me in. Mrs Sheard would produce a glass of orange squash or fizzy lemonade quicker than the spark-man. Mr Sheard would teach me all about gardening, taking great care to show me how to grow poppies from seed, plant out geraniums and pot marigolds. He also had a little vegetable plot at the bottom of his garden where he grew lettuce, carrots, cabbage and potatoes. In his greenhouse he had a row of tomato plants, tall as the metal signs outside the Motorman's Café. Sometimes he would break one off the stems and offer it to me.

If the weather was cold they would take me into the house for a warm drink and a piece of gingercake. It was a very beautiful house, very bright and very roomy. They drank from lovely china cups and saucers, and draped embroidered covers over tables. In the corner beside the dresser stood a big ticking grandfather clock whose brass pendulum swung behind a sparkling glass panel sending ripples of light across the walls. The smell of wax polish, sweet peas and homemade baking always made me want to stay longer.

One Saturday afternoon they introduced me to Malcolm, a well-spoken little boy of about seven. He was wearing grey flannel shorts, a pair of long woollen knee socks and a jazzy pullover, which zigged up and zagged down across his chest with bright colours. I liked him instantly and was soon sliding down the grassy slopes on a long wooden sledge, with him.

♋♋

"Let's go fetch it then." Mammy turned up a little late and more than a little bedraggled. I was going to the Adult School to pick up Nanna's Old Folks' Treat Tea, and had arranged to meet Mammy, who would show me where to go. And as she came sidling along, her crow call preceding her, I felt sorry I'd asked.

Mammy waltzed through the quiet streets of Marsden, shut after dinner as usual on Saturdays, and she was vexed. She muttered about it all up Peel Street, across Manchester Road, further up Peel Street, and across Carrs Road. She was still vexed when we reached the Adult School. Each time she craned her bird neck round to me and opened her beak, the smell of wine flowed out with the vexed – no good ever came of drinking, I remembered Nanna saying each time Mammy had staggered up to our house and staggered back. Poor Mammy, I could just imagine her stalking round her house, supping wine all morning with Topczewski (she'd moved back in with him). Him flapping at her, and her pecking back. No wonder she was vexed. I shut it out of my mind, and went inside to collect the Treat tea.

For a moment, I forgot Mammy and her troubles, and instead peered into the white paper bags I'd been given. Wouldn't Nanna enjoy this? Boiled ham sandwiches in one bag, and a trifle in a frilly wax dish, and a bun in the other.

But then, there was Mammy, nudging me out. "Cum h'on, cum h'on. 'urry up." She began sighing and muttering and seemed to shrink herself right into a shell and roll back down Peel Street. She was smaller and thinner then than I'd ever realised, just a head of raven hair on sparrow legs, scruffy as a starling in her old mac. I wanted to say 'Don't be sad, Mammy', but her ramblings became so vague, they all fitted into one long word, and I wished I was miles away. Knowing Mammy would only come with me as far as Towngate, I picked up speed.

"'old on, 'old on. Don't run h'off like that. What's matter wi' yer? In-a-rush-to-get-back-to-'im are yer."

I slowed to a trot, I wasn't even thinking of stopping off at Mammy's when I knew Topczewski was there. Mammy looked at me then, and her face was a candle and her eyes two wicks. Thank goodness we were nearly home.

All Mammy's mornings vexations bulleted out. 'Bloody this' nearly shattered Moorhouse's window, and 'Bloody that' bounced off the pavement outside Lunn's butchers. I was showered with vexeds and bastards and worse. It was good sense to stay a wingbeat ahead.

We turned round into Market Place. Then Mammy stopped dead and so did my breath. After a moments pause, she puffed out her chest, and squawked "Ah've 'ad enough. I'm gunner end it all. Ah've bloody well 'ad a–bloody-nuff!"

She launched herself right into the road outside Russell's just as a large white van appeared in the corner of my eye, turning out of Peel Street. Then there was a terrible squealing of brakes and more noise than I'd heard in a long time. Wheels skidded, voices shouted, and above it all, was Mammy's bad language. I grabbed the nearest bit of her coat and pulled her back. If only I could have done that with Kathleen.

The van driver had swerved past her, and had stopped, just at the back of the Co-op.

"A yer bloody daft, yer stupid woman! Ah could have flattened yer," yelled the van driver. "Use yer bloody eyes next time."

Mammy swore back at him as he pulled out again and sped off.

I suddenly remembered something else frightening that Mammy had done. Graham had told me once. He couldn't remember how it came about, but one time Arnold, Kathleen and me were very small, Mammy had another mad ig and had sent Graham, who'd only been twelve or thirteen, to owd Mother Orams (our other Grandmother) to tell her she (Mammy) was so vexed with us all that she was going to drown us all in the river. Mammy's fury had terrified Graham then, like it terrified me now.

I walked her back to Towngate and left with her fury still screeching in my ears, but at least the treat tea was still intact.

CHAPTER SIXTEEN

SUMMER '59

Mammy was less vexed when she turned up at Millstone Cottages one Sunday, civil even to the point of accepting a brew when Graham offered to make her one. The real reason for her visit though, was enough to strip her of 'vexed' for all time, and clothe me with it.

"I've t'meet Wainwright," she said, "An' ah'm tekin' you wi' mi on t'next down'ill bus. So do summet wi' that 'air."

I remembered seeing my father last year, walking down Peel Street past the Mechanics, in a straight line too, despite what Mammy always said of him. In a shabby suit and cloth cap he could only have been my father. He'd obviously seen me running along before I'd seen him, and had been gathering the courage to say hello, for the word – when it came - was shaky, and he'd looked down straight away. I'd muttered a quick reply, and that was that. He was off in the direction of Manchester Road and I'd ran across Brougham Road and into Nellie's without another thought.

"Get a move h'on," Mammy was twittering.

I raked my fingers through my hair, straightening out the smaller lugs[*] and leaving the big ones, then trailed out after Mammy to the bus stop.

We got off at Longroyd Bridge, just before town, and went to stand by a hairdresser's.

"'e should be 'ere in about five minutes, if that bus were h'on time," Mammy said, fiddling with her hairslide. I glanced around at dull cars, and dismal house fronts. Lollipop sticks clogged up the gutter. The rest of the pavement in front of Mammy was patched with a flattened Woodbine packet and some cardboard.

"Does Wainwright work there?" I pointed to the gaunt mill opposite.

"Ah don't know what 'es doin'," Mammy replied "H'all ah know is, 'e were a moulder at France an' Brooks h'at Crimble from when 'e left school t'when 'e joined up. 'e were in h'Eygypt, yer know."

I did know. I also knew where Egypt was. To Mammy, it was just a name. I watched her hop about on the pavement and fiddle with her hairgrip again. Should I plan in my head what to say to Wainwright, if he came? But keeping quiet might be best. Mammy might do enough squawking for both of us.

I tried to imagine what it might have been like to walk in the house at

---

[*] *Knots.*

Towngate that day three years ago, and swap Topczewski for Wainwright. Wainwright could have said, "Let's find th'iron fer yer mother," led me into the kitchen and cheerfully found the iron, with no mention of chimneys. But I couldn't really picture it, and instead shook blood and soot away, and started to count cars till my real father turned up, if he ever did.

I'd got as far as twenty-seven and couldn't be bothered with anymore. My ball was in my pocket, real and safe, so I took it out and ran up and down the pavement with it for a bit to stop my legs from stiffening up.

"'e'll 'ave bloody well forgot." Mammy shifted about on her feet, and rubbed her chin, then picked at her nails and pulled at tufts of dark hair. "Just like when h'our Graham were a boy. 'e were supposed t'be meetin' us t'give us some money fer food, but 'e never came. It were middle er winter an' all, an' we hadn't even enough t'buy a quartren er Tyfool tea. Well, a won't a-tolerate it. I'm not havin' that sort er work."

"I wish Arnold were 'ere," I moaned. Mammy said nothing.

By and by, the next down'ill bus from Oldham rattled past. We'd been waiting an hour. I was about to suggest going home, when Mammy announced a plan to walk further back up the road, toward the railway bridge and picture house. I sighed and followed.

We hadn't gone far, when a dull figure unfolded from a shop doorway, wearing the same tired expression as Mammy.

"Bloody 'ell, Kitty, ah'd nearly given yer up," said Wainwright.

"'eh," shrieked Mammy, and I shrank back expecting war to break out. "We've been waitin' h'over there an hour."

There'd obviously been a mix-up about the meeting place, but Wainwright let it go, and seemed pleased to see us. In turn, Mammy quickly re-arranged her ruffled feathers, and started chattering and being normal. I walked a couple of paces behind, following both my parents for the first time – straight into a pub!

This was no back door job to buy brandy for Nanna. Mammy said "Cum on 'eather," and pushed me boldly inside the main entrance. It wasn't too bright inside, and people were made hazy by all the smoke. Cigarettes hung from the mouths of grey faces, streaming dragon breath when they spoke or laughed, each grey word from each grey face springing up to form a washing line of ayes, yusses and no's from different conversations. These mouths were never empty. When smoke and words weren't spilling out, beer was swilling in.

I stayed close to Mammy as she led us through a thicket of loud men and women, and precarious pint glasses, to a seat at the back, and shrank into it, banging my ball a bit on the table. Wainwright returned with the drinks for himself and Mammy, and a glass of lemonade and a packet of potato crisps for me, which I carefully timed to make last till finally it looked like Mammy and

Wainwright were ready to go.

"We're goin' a-visitin' yer Auntie h'Alice" Said Mammy. Somewhere, deep inside myself, where no-one else could see, I pulled a face.

"When we get there," Wainwright fiddled with the wet rim of his empty glass, "Can yer call me... Dad?"

My inside face pulled even further, and the sloshing together of lemonade and potato crisps didn't feel quite as good.

We caught a bus to Linfit Steps* to see Auntie Alice. Clutching my ball, I stepped into the house of Wainwright's sister and smelt the remains of Sunday dinner. Auntie Alice was plumper than Wainwright, and far chattier. She sat us down on a firm settee, and paraded round her clean living room offering tea, and dandelion and burdock.

I sat quiet for most of the time, wondering how I could ever come out and say that word I had to say. Wainwright must've sensed my discomfort, and kept asking questions to try and prompt me. I wanted to say it, just once, to cheer Wainwright up (He had slouched right over, and looked really miserable like a poor character in Rupert who'd lost his way.) Mammy and Auntie Alice were chuntering about summet, and every so often Wainwright would mutter too, and glance at me with brown puppy eyes. They reminded me much of Arnold's that afer he'd blundered his way through some sentence, adding "'aven't you, 'eather?" I squeezed my ball tight.

"Yes Dad."

The words were no more than two squeaks, and I immediately felt hot and even more awkward. That was it though, I'd said it and Wainwright beamed so Rupertly that I was glad I'd said it. I'd made him happy. 'That Wainwright, who spends all my maintainance money in the Swan or The Griffin' (the place we'd been today) as Mammy described him. I hoped it would last him his lifetime, for there was no way those words could come out again.

As we left, Auntie Alice flicked her hand over the cushions I'd sat on which were still puffing back to shape after I'd stood up.

❧❧

One day, when Malcolm and I were playing 'Cowboys n' Indian's' down by the stream, his mother called him in and said that it was time to go. I'd never met her before, but she didn't look like either Malcolm or his grandparents.

"We're going your way, Heather," said Mrs Sheard. "Malcolm and his mum are going to catch the bus at the top of Private Road. You might as well come with us."

---

* *Between Slaithwaite and Linthwaite.*

Their daughter-in-law screwed up her nose when she saw me.

We had just got to the top of the cobbly bit where I did most of my 'stickin' when she suddenly noticed I had a grubby bandage tied around the first finger of my right hand.

"Urghh! What's that?" She scowled.

"Ah cut mi finger on a tin er sardines last week."

"But it's filthy. Why don't you go home and put a clean dressing on?"

"Shhh," said Mrs Sheard quietly, "you'll upset her."

"Well it is filthy – look at it. And look at the state of her dress - *that's filthy as well.*"

I could see Mrs Sheard was deeply embarrassed and immediately tried to smooth things over.

"She's alright, leave her alone."

"I don't want Malcolm playing with her any more." I heard her whisper again to the old lady. "She's dirty."

Instead of walking all the way to the bus stop with them I took a short cut past the 'owd 'ouse and up the step. When I got in, I decided something had to be done about being mucky. I must wash! I had only seen washing done once though and that was before Nanna had become bedridden. It had been a beautiful sunny day and Nanna had taken out the dolly tub, the rubbing board, and a posser.* Nanna and I had made endless journeys across the moor to fetch water, which we had boiled in the old copper kettle over a stick fire, and tipped into the dolly tub – a big zinc barrel with deep ridges around it. We'd possed most of the stuff. The rest, like Graham's overall's, she had rubbed along the rubbing board with a bar of green soap and a scrubbing brush. Nanna didn't have a mangle to wring the clothes out so we had to squeeze them as hard as we could. There were no pegs or washing line either. We had simply laid the clothes on the grass in the hot sun and waited for them to dry. Every now and then Nanna had said, "Cum on love, let's go n' turn them there clothes," and we had slipped across the road and onto the moor. Very soon the clothes had become crisp and dry and smelt of Fairy Soap and sunshine.

Nanna was unable to get up now so I would just have to do it myself. I had an idea though. Perhaps I could get away with the all the complicated bits of washing and just iron summet. I knew we had an iron. I'd seen it many times, underneath the stairs; it was a heavy cast iron thing, dusty and rusty.

When I explained to Nanna what I intended to do she said that I would have to clean the iron first. "Get a bit of old rag and rub it as hard as you can."

---

* *A long stick with a copper head attached, to agitate washing in a bowl, and stamp out water afterwards.*

After taking it from the shelf in the pantry and doing my very best with it for a good ten minutes, there was a *slight* improvement. Now all I needed to do was warm it up. This meant a trip down Private Road, stickin'. I got the fire going by holding the 'draw tin' up to the opening and throwing a few cobs of coal on.

"Put t'iron on t'rib and ah'll tell yer when ah think it's warm enough," said Nanna.

I'd seen 'electric' irons in a shop in Marsden. I also knew that Robin Starch made your washing as stiff as a board and that Persil washed 'whiter than white'. But I would just have to make do with what we had. Under Nanna's instructions I placed a piece of old rag on the kitchen table and began to iron. Nanna looked quite worried when I took the iron off the rib. "Remember it's hot," she said, and I ended up with my beautiful navy dress with the sprinkling of daisies, from the rag pile slightly less wrinkled, but just as mucky as the one I had on.

PART 5

CHAPTER SEVENTEEN

AUTUMN '59

Around three o'clock one bright October afternoon, Mammy blew through the door like an ill wind. She hardly had time to say hello before rushing into the kitchen, returning moments later with the old enamel basin and the ladling can full of cold water.

"Cum on 'eather, get yer 'ands n' face washed," she said. "Ah'm, tekin yer t'town.

Drops splashed onto the pegged rug as she began teeming the water out of the tin jug and into the chipped bowl. "Cum on 'urry up, ah want t'get h'off."

"'ere we go agen," I thought.

Nanna propped herself up onto one elbow. "Where are yer goin' Kitty?"

"Town," said Mammy sharply. " Were goin' t'town."

There was something about the way she said that which made me think she was up to summet.

"Cum on!" She thrust my hands into the bowl of cold water. "Get them mucky 'ands washed."

"Ah can wash em miself."

"Well get on wi' it then," she snapped. "An' where's that frock ah got yer from t'jumble sale t'other week – t'one wi green h'apples on?" She didn't wait for my reply, marching instead into the kitchen and rummaging around in the pile of old rags. Minutes later she emerged with the 'green h'apple dress' dangling over her arm.

"'ere, tek that mucky skirt n' jumper off," she said, throwing the only slightly cleaner dress at me. "An' put this on."

"But …" I began.

"Just do it!"

I didn't know what had got into her. Even Nanna was muttering and shaking her head.

As I slipped my arms out of the grubby jumper, Mammy ran to the window and began swaying with agitation as she peered down the road. She didn't move. But by the time I'd pulled my dress over my head, she'd hopped over to the slop bucket and was tipping out the water from the bowl. Summet was up.

Next thing I knew there was a knock on the door and Miss Newton and Mr Bruce walked in.

"Come along, Heather," said Miss Newton. "You're coming with us."

Mammy flew round the room, twittering, and everything was in a flummox.

"Let's get out of here," I heard Bossy Bruce say, and Miss Newton took my hand and led me out.

I looked back, bewildered. Nanna had raised herself up and was calling out "Where are yer teckin' 'er." Mammy had her back turned. Bruce banged the door between my family and me, behind it I heard raised voices, which faded the further away I got.

They shut me in the back of the car and I didn't dare to ask where they were taking me. Miss Newton and Mr Bruce chatted to each other in the front seats, and never gave me another thought. We ended up in Huddersfield. I recognised some of the buildings from the time I'd come down to the market to buy half a pound of fig biscuits and a bag of mushrooms.

Mr Bruce pulled up in a street full of shops, opposite a frowning church.

"Come on Heather," said Miss Newton again, turning around to face me. "We're getting out here." She opened the door and I had no choice but to follow. Mr Bruce stayed in the car, and I was glad. I found myself drowned by a tall building with a wide doorway and two ugly gargoyles that glared right at me.

"Heather," they seemed to leer, "they're going to lock you up."

Miss Newton urged me through green doors and up two flights of stone steps to a small landing. Here were two more doors, behind which lay what? Corridors I'd never find the end of? The land of the Imps of Spring? Or doors, and doors, and doors? Miss Newton held her hand out, encouraged me forward, but instead I saw the shadow of Rupert, flitting fearlessly ahead, and I followed him into some sort of small reception area, where the light glared more brightly than the gargoyles. At one end of the room was a window with two frosted glass panels. Screwed to a ledge below the window was a monstrous brown bell. Above this, dark letters demanded 'Press For Attention'. Miss Newton pressed and a young lady slid open one of the frosted panels.

"We're here to see the doctor, " said Miss Newton.

The receptionist disappeared through another door and I could hear low voices, probably talking about me. The other room was small and dark. There was a hard bed shrouded with a sterile sheet. At the far end of the room was a blue screen like a concertina. Beside it a small desk. Moments later, a tall gentleman with greying hair came in, wearing a white smock and carrying some pieces of paper. It was not doctor Hande. In the top pocket of his smock the lid of a fountain pen poked out.

"Hello," he said, taking the fountain pen from his pocket and removing the lid. "I'd like to make sure you're not ill or anything." He put the bits of paper down on the desk and asked for my date of birth.

I mumbled, my chin poking into my chest. "Ninth er September."

"Nine, nine, forty nine," announced Miss Newton, extracting a sheet of paper from her brown leather briefcase.

I shrank into myself as he examined my chest and back with a cold stethoscope. After looking down my throat and in my ears he inspected my hair, like the nit nurse did at school.

"She's a bit thin." I heard him mutter to Miss Newton as I fastened the rubber buttons on my mucky liberty bodice.

Dusk was brushing the edges of Huddersfield by the time we returned to Mr Bruce's car. All I could think about was flopping on the horsehair couch when I got home, but when we turned off the main road and travelled along a confusion of winding streets I knew we were not heading for Marsden. Shadows leapt in at me through the car windows, biting me with dark and fear. They grabbed my shoulders and shook me around each bend, pushing me one way, then another. They wanted to jump down my throat and choke me. A strange building with round towers and queer gables lurched past before we rounded a corner. Then we stopped, and the shadows slipped back out of the windows and hung about in the twilight. The headlights picked out haunched shapes of six Victorian houses, a bit like the Vicarage in Marsden.

Turning to Miss Newton, Mr Bruce said, "This shouldn't take long, then I'll take you back to Huddersfield to pick your car up."

Miss Newton opened all the darkness back on me, and I struggled to climb out into it. "Come on, Heather," she said. "Don't be frightened, there's lots of other little girls here for you to play with. You'll be well fed and well looked after. You'll soon get used to it."

Well looked after! What was she talking about? My heart punched the inside of my chest so hard I put my hand there in case Miss Newton saw it. I wanted to ask what was going on, but my tongue didn't.

Mr Bruce knocked on the door. Very soon I could hear the sound of footsteps and the key being turned; then the door opened and an elderly lady in a dark dress and loose woollen cardigan filled the space, a surge apron was fastened firmly around her small waist.

"Hello, we've brought Heather," said Mr Bruce, almost cheerfully.

Brought Heather where? Why wouldn't they tell me? I wanted to cry but my eyes wouldn't.

"Come in. Come in, I've been expecting you," said the lady in the apron. "Beech Towers rang earlier to say you were coming."

She led us through a small kitchen, which smelt of stale cabbage and mashed potatoes. It was like school dinners. The elderly lady then opened a door into an enormous room that was brightly lit and wick with girls - about twelve of them. They all stopped what they were doing and ran up. I was drowned in a sea of clean frocks.

"Now then, give Heather a bit of room." The old lady pushed them aside.

"Is she stoppin'?" Asked a thin girl with dark hair and round glasses who had somehow managed to push her way to the front and refused to budge.

"Yes. So you'll have plenty of time to talk to her later."

So this was it; I'd been 'tecken away' like our Arnie. Neither Nanna, nor even Graham could help me now. I stood there trembling and small.

Miss Newton opened her briefcase and passed the old lady some bits of paper. "You'll need these," she said. "They're Heather's Free From Infection details."

"I've saved you some tea, Heather," said the lady. "Sit down here and I'll bring it in." She pointed to a table, which reminded me of a picture in a book at school called 'The Last Supper'. I wasn't hungry.

"We'll get off then." Miss Newton made for the door. "And let Heather get on with her tea." She came over and touched me on the shoulder. "Take care, Heather, and don't worry, Auntie Eileen'll soon make you feel at home." I hung my head in silence.

Some of the girls were sitting on the floor watching a black and white television set. After nibbling at the cheese sandwich and sipping a drop of tea, Auntie Eileen said that I could leave the table and watch the end of 'King Billy'.

"Sit by me," urged the girl with short black hair and round glasses. She reminded me of 'Dilly Day Dreem' in my 'School Friend Annual' I'd left behind. I didn't watch King Billy, I was too busy thinking how it had been with Arnold. Had he missed us like we'd missed him? Had he been forced to eat like I had been? Maybe he'd planned to run away. I was jerked out of my thoughts as a bundle of clothes and a pair of striped pyjamas were dumped in my lap. Then I was taken on a quick tour of the home.

"Here's t'kitchen, an' room yer've just been sitting in is t'dining room. This is t'washroom. You must leave the sink clean and put yer towel back neat on the peg."

Six stripy towels hung like six nativity Josephs opposite the six sinks.

"Your bed is in the small dormitory." She led me across the landing and into a large bedroom containing six single beds. "And this is your bed." She pointed to one at the far end. "Put your clothes on the chair beside it... and when you've done that come into the bathroom, you're having a bath. Bring your pyjama's with you."

Having a bath! The words knotted in my stomach with the sandwiches I hadn't wanted. Whatever would Nanna think of this?

Some of the other girls had followed us up and were taking off their skirts and jumpers and putting on their nightclothes. Dilly Day Dreem, whose real name turned out to be Jean Livesey, trailed behind me like a yappy dog.

The bathroom was big and cold. Huge black and white tiles covered the floor and little shiny ones covered the walls. Auntie Eileen was already filling the bath. Steam rose to the ceiling like thick fog.

I'd never had a bath before and wasn't looking forward to one now. Once in, I hunched up trembling, a skeleton of grey tide marks like the one round the bath. Auntie Eileen poured a jug of water over my head, then tipped some carbolic shampoo onto the palm of her hand and began rubbing my hair with it. It stank. Another jug of water splashed over my head to rinse it off. Next she scrubbed me from head to toe with a little wooden nailbrush; paying special attention to the muck roak around my neck and on my hands. She even dug out 'potatoes', (which were apparently growing in my ears) with the corner of a flannel. Then, paying no attention to the girls gawping through the open door as they passed, she handed me a large white towel and told me to get dry. I hid behind the towel, drying myself quickly as girls stared.

Back downstairs, I was given a glass of cold milk and two biscuits. I didn't want them.

The bed covers, when I got between them were stiff with starch and had that newly washed smell, and each bed had a fawn blanket and a green and cream counterpane. I was told that everyone was responsible for making their own bed, tucking in proper hospital corners. If it wasn't right, there'd be heck to pay. I'd have rather been in Nanna's dark little cottage, sleeping on the mucky tickin.

That night I couldn't sleep. I kept thinking of Mammy's lies, Nanna's horrified face as they bundled me away from her, the visit to the doctor's, the sinister car journey and the faces of the other girls as I walked through the door.

❧ ❧

My very first morning at the Home, I woke to a loud donging sound coming from the foot of the stairs. I was shocked upright. Someone, somewhere, jumped out of bed, scurried towards the door, flicked on the light switch then padded back. Some of the other girls threw off their counterpanes and· scrambled to the edge of their mattresses. One girl dived out of bed and made a dash for the lavatory. By the time I got there, everyone else had too and were shoving me out of the way till I was the last of twelve. When I trailed back into the dormitory, everyone else was putting on their school uniform (blue blouse, long socks, smoke-grey gymslips), I reached across to my chair and sorted through the clothes I had been issued with the night before.

Jean Livesey had woken up in a bad mood and began bossing me about.

"Go and wash yerself and clean yer teeth!" She followed me into the bathroom and stood over me while I did it. "Not like that... like this!" She yanked the toothbrush out of my hand and began scrubbing my teeth with it - up down, up down, and definitely not like the funniest clown. I felt like a two-year-old, but daren't say so. "Now go and make your bed," she commanded.

Again, I did exactly as I was told and began straightening the covers as best I could. "That won't do!" Said Little Miss Bossy Britches. "See these corners? They're supposed to look like this. And this bit's supposed to look like that... then tuck this in 'ere... do this, do that." She was horrible. She'd obviously had plenty of practice in making beds *and* dishing out orders. That done - she said it was time to go downstairs for breakfast.

The big oak table had already been set. In the centre was a large white milk jug, a bowl full of sugar and two little glass salt and pepper pots. Some girls were already sitting at the table waiting for their breakfast. I wasn't sure what to do so I just stood in the middle of the floor twiddling my hair.

"Sit down, Heather," said Auntie Eileen as she passed me on her way backward and forwards to the kitchen. I sat as near to the edge of the bench as I could. I didn't want to be boxed in.

Breakfast was a bowl of porridge, followed by bacon and egg and two rounds of tomato. A slice of buttered bread rested on the side of each plate. At home a meal the size of this would have fed us for a week! But I wasn't hungry, and couldn't eat it.

"Come on, Heather," said Auntie Eileen. "Stop messing about. You're not allowed to leave the table until you've done... and we haven't all day, so hurry up."

I stared at my food, and the cutlery stamped with W.R.C.C.* Some of the other girls were already scraping their plates and asking if they could please leave the table and put their plates in the sink. The place was a mad house. Umpteen girls began shouting things like, "So and so has pinched mi school pumps, I've lost mi satchel, where's mi coat and who's 'ad mi shoes." Jean (thank goodness) had left the table and was busy preparing to leave the house.

"You won't be going to school today, Heather," said Auntie Eileen. "New girls stay indoors for at least twenty four hours. For 'eavens sake get that porridge eaten."

The Cottage Homes, six of them, were made of sandstone, blackened over the years with soot and grime. On dull, wet days they looked even more dark and depressing. The roofs sloped up for ever and had three sinsiter gables protruding

---

* *West Riding County Council.*

from both front and back. Each Home was solid, identical in shape and size, and held up to a dozen children – sixty-four altogether. The Homes were divided up into three for the boys and three for the girls. They had stuck me in 'Home One'. A low stone wall seperated the Girl's Homes from the Boy's Homes and it was woe-be-tide if any of the boys were found on the wrong side of the fence.

Compared to Nanna's pokey windows, the tall sashes and stone lintels were enormous. They were clean and bright and littered with squashed noses trying to get a squint at the new girl.

Auntie Eileen began clearing the breakfast table and washing up. The last of the girls; who looked about fourteen, buttoned her coat, tied her shoelaces and disappeared through the door.

At last the Home was quiet and I managed to pluck up the courage to ask if I could go for a walk.

"Ah won't go far," I promised.

"No! I've already told you - it's house rules. You won't be going out until at least tomorrow." Her voice was sharp and cold. I'd heard of people putting butter on cat's paws to stop them from straying and this was what she was doing to me. Although she was as old as Nanna, she was nowhere as nice.

There was little else to do but follow the old woman around. "Wen will ah be goin' 'ome then?" I asked quietly. "Yer see me Nanna needs me, she's nubdi t'look after 'er only our Graham. An' 'es at work all day... Will ah be goin' 'ome next week?"

"No!"

"Will it be t'week after?"

"No! Now will you be quiet? You're not going anywhere."

She bent over the sink and began scrubbing the porridge pan like she'd scrubbed me last night. "It's my last day, and I've got a lot to do, so go sit down and don't make a muff." There was a small tremor in her voice as she sprinkled some Panshine on to her cloth.

The settee seemed the best place to go and do nothing. Auntie Eileen strode in with the Mansion Polish, and I watched her flap, wipe and move from one corner gradually round to the next. In a shaft of light from the window, I saw grey dust waterfall off the top of the television and flicker in the air, like the television screen sometimes when it was on. Then Auntie Eileen vigorously swept the floor, as if the dust was annoying her. You could have almost swept the dust out of her wrinkles.

"Lift," she said when the broom reached my feet. I lifted. Eventually she went, and I heard clanks and clonks from the kitchen.

I watched the dust spiral in the shaft of light. If I could step into it and part the curtain, I might find myself in Nutwood, surrounded by as much green as it was possible to see with two eyes. I ran through the frames of each picture, till all there were, were rolling hills and clumps of trees. Arms spread, like I was my aeroplane, I dived towards a group of people playing cricket: Rupert and his chums. Edward Trunk, Bill Badger, Rastus Mouse, Tigerlily. I stopped on the edge to watch, like an outsider or The Invisible Man.

"Heather!"

The cricket game faded, and I was on the settee again.

"There's a cheese sandwich and a drink of tea on the table for you." Auntie shouted through from the kitchen. "And make sure you eat it today!"

I wasn't hungry.

At about two o'clock the new housemother walked in, a knitting needle woman with string arms, hair the colour of raffia, and a face full of thread veins.

"I'm Auntie Flossy," she rumbled. "I'm teckin' over today." I was left alone then to wonder how best to avoid this woman, and retreated back to the settee.

I was still there around teatime when the girls clattered through the door.

After tea (which I could only pick at), the television went on and everyone crowded round to watch 'The Man From Laramie'. When it came time for Auntie Eileen to leave there were tears in her eyes. Briskly though and without a fuss, she said goodbye and Jean Livesey appeared to be one of the most difficult to leave. Jean cried herself to sleep that night. Apparently she had known Auntie Eileen since she was two. I suppose she had grown very fond of the old lady and probably looked on her as a mother. When I tried to be kind and ask what was the matter, she bit my head off, so I didn't dare ask her again.

After forcing down some breakfast the following day, Auntie Flossy took me to a monstrous chest next to the hallway. "Clothes are in 'ere," she said, flinging the door open. "Winter stuff this side, summer stuff that." I stared at rows of tweed coats, woollen skirts and dresses and trim piles of folded dull-coloured jumpers. "On May first, we get summer stuff out..." I glanced at the summer side; print dresses, spun rayon skirts and Bry Nylon cardigans, and shuddered at the thought of having to share clothes with all those girls. New Auntie hadn't finished. She opened a drawer full of underskirts, vests and knickers, adding "Blue for winter, pink for summer." Perhaps Graham or Mammy would turn up before long and take me home, before I got chance to wear the Bry Nylon cardigans and everyone elses pink knickers. Then Auntie said I could go out and play. "But you mustn't leave the grounds," she said. She gave me a dark green gabardine, similar to the one I had brought with me, and a pair of sturdy lace-up shoes, size thirteen. I was told to leave my crepe-soled sandals on the sheet of old newspaper in the kitchen and *never* to wear them outside. I could forego wearing the only nice things I had now, at least I was out of doors in the fresh air, such as it was.

But Graham and Mammy didn't turn up, and instead I had to learn the routine. All our files were kept in the office downstairs, and no-one was allowed to sneak in and look. Jean Livesey, who had turned from a yappy dog into a nippy, bitey one, told me that someone had once, and had been dragged to the storeroom where the cornflakes were kept, beaten with a broom, and locked in till morning. Then another girl told Jean she was a liar, and a row started, so I sloped away quick.

All around me now were houses, chimney pots and big sash windows. The homes stood in about an acre of land, some of which was tarmac and some scrubland. A high stone wall ran along the perimeter of the grounds and separated the Cottage Homes from the outside world. Set in a patch of tarmac at the top of the field were three swings, each with a little wooden seat and rusty chains. These were the 'girls' swings'. At the bottom of the drive, but still on the grassland, were three 'boys' swings'. Chattering children gathered in little groups like they did in the school playground. Some were playing catch with a bald tennis ball whilst a group of other girls twisted a long skipping rope round and round, chanting,

'I'm a little Girl Guide dressed in blue,
These are the actions you must do...'

I spied Jean Livesey with some others, leaning against a wall puffing away on sweet cigarettes. Within seconds they'd stopped what they were doing, and swarmed around me.

"What's your name?" Asked one of them.

"She's called Heather and she's my best friend. Aren't you?" Said Jean Livesey.

"Yes," I lied.

"Heather? That's a funny name," cackled one of the girls. I was a bit shocked, no one had ever said this before.

One of the girls, a pasty, fair-haired girl from Home Two, with pink National Health spectacles, introduced herself as Meryl. She was about the same age and height as me.

The following morning Jean told me that I was going to Sunday school with her, Meryl and Cynthia.

"You'll be able t'wear yer best clothes," she said.

She was right. Auntie Flossy shouted me across the room and took me into the clothing closet.

"We'll find you an outfit for Sunday school," she said. Next thing I knew, she had rooted out a red tartan kilt, a green jumper and a pair of fawn socks.

"She can't 'ave them," snarled one of the girls who had followed us in. "I usually wear them."

"Well you're not wearing them today," snapped Auntie Flossy as she held them up to me to see if they would fit. "You can wear summet else."

"But that's not fair!" stamped the girl. "I want to wear them."

"I've told you before – 'I want' never gets."

The girl marched off slamming the door behind her.

"Bad tempered little devil," muttered Auntie Flossy. "Now try this coat on, Heather. It should fit you."

The coat was slate green tweed with a black velvet collar and a strip of velvet on the pocket flaps.

"Yer, that's alright." She glanced up and down as I stood stiff in the smart coat.

"Leave it 'ere on t'hook but tek t'kilt an' tother stuff upstairs and get changed." She shoved the bundle of clothes into my arms. "And put your dirty clothes in the laundry bag at the foot of the stairs.

As I walked across the landing to the dormitory, I noticed the bathroom door was ajar, and Jean Livesey, a slit inside, was buttoning up her blouse.

"Come 'ere n' fasten these fer me," she barked as I tried to creep past.

No 'please', or 'would you mind'. I groaned inwardly at her manners, till I'd pushed the bathroom door open.

The buttons, not much bigger than a small pearl, had to be fastened through a tiny loop about the same size as the eye of a needle. As Jean was taller than me, I couldn't reach very well. She reacted by flinging her arms about and screaming.

"Stand on t'buffet."

And she'd seemed so nice days earlier.

But even with the extra height of the buffet, I could not fasten the buttons. In the end my fingers became so numb it was impossible. Jean spun round, knocked me off the buffet and sent me crashing into the door. Shocked and dazed I picked myself up and only managed to stop myself from crying by thinking of how she'd lay into me if she saw tears.

"Yer useless bugger," she raged. "Get away from me… ah'll do it meself."

Sunday school was about five minutes away, along a narrow ginnel that ran alongside the Homes and down Birkdale Road. Meryl and Jean said we would be sitting at the front. We had each been given sixpence for the collection.

"I'm not putting mine in," said Meryl.

Jean, who had learnt a lot about religion from Auntie Eileen said, "That's dishonest and if you're dishonest, you'll never go t'heaven."

I wondered if the same applied to being horrible.

"I'm not bothered," stated Meryl, "Hell'll do for me if I can 'ave a quarter of sweets instead, so there."

The church was large and cold when we stepped inside, and smelt of dust and damp hymn books. Most of the congregation was already seated, capless men with women in toffee paper hats. They stared at us as we walked in. Jean and Meryl slid into the front pew after a bit of pushing, and started fratching over a red leather pillowy thing.

Then the service began, and I spent the time counting how many times Meryl kicked my ankles. "Tell an' yer dead," she whispered. After a long, boring hymn and a few prayers, the vicar decided to include us in his sermon.

Looking first at Meryl and then at me, he said in the same voice as Big Ben when I'd heard it on the wireless, "I want you two girls to look at each other and make a wish. You…" he motioned to Meryl, "say to the girl on your right (me) I wish, I wish, your wish comes true. Go on." Meryl's hands began to shake and she turned an interesting shade of geranium pink. She glared at me as she stammered out words she didn't mean, and when I had to reply "I wish, I wish, the same to you" I got confused and it came out wrong, but I'd said it so quiet that no-one would have heard. It was apparent, later, that Meryl's wish had come true, she'd made my ankles black and blue. But my wish hadn't happened.

Instead of making jam 'n' bread at Millstone Cottage, I was making roads in mashed potato with a W.R.C.C. fork in Home One.

The following day, I was given a gymslip, a blue blouse and a pair of long grey socks, and sent to a new school. Auntie Flossy said she would be going with me: just-to-make-sure-that-I-got-there.

I hadn't been let through the big gates before, but it was just as much of a prison outside them as in. A long road with semi-detached prisons with their own walls. To the left – the direction in which we were going – the long road continued, like one of those awful corridors where Miss Newton took me. From here the hospital seemed even bigger than I had first imagined and stretched almost the full length of Heald's Road. Its Gothic towers seemed to pierce the sky.

A dozen or so of other girls from Homes One, Two and Three skipped along beside us. Jean was amongst them. They were chattering on about teenage dolls but I couldn't join in. The trees down Heald's Road were smaller than my trees down Private Road End – more stunted, and sad. Pathetic little trees in an ugly street. How was everyone at home? But there'd only be Nanna, and Graham when he was in. Maybe Graham was missing me emptying the slop bucket now he'd have to do it for himself.

At the end of the road was a junction. Here we went straight on, past a little sweet shop on the corner and along a narrow pavement that led us down a slight incline and into a housing estate. From here I could see the rooftops of what I assumed to be Dewsbury Moor School, and I was flayed[*] to death. The yard was a hive of buzzing children and here came me, preparing to get stung.

After a quick meeting in the headmaster's office (whereupon Auntie Flossy informed him of my date of birth and current address), I was put in the hands of an older girl with good manners who had been assigned to take me to my classroom.

"Come straight home with Jean and Meryl," called Auntie Flossy after me. "No playing about. Straight home, remember."

"Yes," I muttered.

What did Auntie Flossy know about 'home'? I should be running back down the fragrant canal bank, bursting to tell Nanna what I'd done, but instead trawling down a grey straight street behind Meryl and Jean, and entering a loveless house of nasty girls.

The classroom was musty and badly lit with double desks and pointed windows. Meryl, Cynthia and Jean had already told me that we'd all be in the same class so I wasn't surprised to see them. They were sitting one in front of the other at the far end of the classroom. Mr Good the teacher was small and chalky with black corkscrew hair but did indeed seem good. He sat me by one of the

---

[*] *Scared.*

high windows and if he ever saw me staring out, dreaming of Nanna, horses and freedom, must have ignored it, and instead helped me out with my work. My vocabulary was extremely poor, my general knowledge non-existent. He even had to teach me how to write the letter 'a' properly. (Apparently I was starting at the top and going clockwise instead of starting at the top and going anticlockwise.) My nerves must have shown because Mr Good said, "Don't worry, it's not your fault. You've never been shown the proper way that's all."

I think he knew that I liked both reading and writing – even though I wasn't much good at them; and encouraged me by putting 'very good' at the bottom of my exercise books and giving me a positive comment every time I read to him.

One thing Mr Good taught me was never to go beyond the 'punch line' when writing a short story (or something similar.) "It will ruin the ending," he said.

One day during school playtime I found myself chatting to a girl who didn't live in 'The Homes'.

"I'm Valerie," she'd smiled, and suggested that we both sneak into an empty classroom. The door creaked: slowly we opened it and tip-toed in. Valerie tittered as she closed it behind us. We found ourselves in a small, dark room cluttered with ink-blotched desks, piles of exercise books and the smell of chalk. It seemed strangely quiet after the busy playground. As we crept around, Valerie seemed more interested in snooping to sitting and reading.

Except for Jean Livesey's leather bound bible, there were no books or comics in the Home. The other girls didn't seem to bother, but I'd had books and comics all my life and now I longed to sit and read 'Black Bob', The Four Marys and Harold Hare. I missed my 'Bunty' too. So when I saw the solid oak bookcase, stuffed from top to bottom with books; big books, small books and books that seemed so ancient they might have been read by someone as old as Queen Victoria, I began to scan the titles as quickly as possible. Most of them weren't very interesting and had boring titles like 'The World Atlas', 'Roman Britain' and 'British Kings and Queens'. But there, lying flat on its back on the middle shelf was 'Ameliaranne – Bridesmaid'! I couldn't believe it. I had an 'Ameliaranne' book at home – 'Ameliaranne and the Jumble Sale'. I had read it so often that nearly all the pages had worn out. Gingerly I stretched out my hand and took the book from the shelf, terrified that at any minute this little bit of pleasure would be snatched from me. Thumbing quickly through the beautiful pages, I shuffled crabwise to the nearest desk and pulled out a chair.

'It was the first day of the summer holidays, and Ameliaranne was feeling full of happiness'. The opposite page showed a picture of Ameliaranne Stiggins, an angelic little girl with bubbly brown hair and wrinkled stockings. (She reminded me of my friend Patricia Blackburn in Marsden) Ameliaranne was playing with another of the little Stiggins'. Her mother, a whispy woman with sharp features, had grey hair twisted into a neat bun. She was pegging out washing. For a moment, I was almost on our old horsehair couch, running my hand over the washed out water-coloured pictures.

Valerie kept whispering to me across the room, "Look at this," and "have you seen that?" But like an absent-minded professor I would just nod and grunt. Nothing could distract me.

All too soon we heard the sound of the school bell clanging. My accomplice clattered across the classroom, banging into desks and chairs shouting "Come on quick, we'll get done if we're caught in here." She flung the door open while I ran over to reluctantly deposit Ameliaranne on the shelf where I'd found her. Together we beat a hasty retreat into the playground.

❧ ❧

Every morning around eight, a porter from Beech Towers, the hospital over the road, would wheel a trolley across to The Homes which contained six three-gallon milk churns. Whoever happened to be on milk duty that day would take two three-pint milk jugs from the kitchen cupboard, run outside and fill both jugs with the ladling can. The milk was stored in the fridge in the kitchen.

Potatoes also came from Beech Towers. They arrived in a large steel bowl and had already been peeled in a large automatic peeler down at the hospital. But the peeler was unable to 'eye' the potatoes so we all had to do it. The potatoes were kept in freezing cold water to stop them from going brown. Our little fingers soon became lumps of ice as we stood at the kitchen sink poking the tip of the vegetable knife into the bad eyes and flicking them out.

Food was delivered to the home in a large wicker basket. Cheese came in big whopping blocks and cornflakes were packed in big grey boxes with 'Not for Resale' stamped on the side in large black letters. No one ever went to the shop to 'buy in': not even for something as simple as a loaf of bread or a bag of sugar.

Another thing to appear from over the road was Matron, at teatimes once a week. She'd waft in like some big bird with a 'I hope you're all behaving yourselves girls', a couple of quick words with Auntie Doreen and Auntie Flossy who'd smile, nod and say "Yes Matron" or "Of course, Matron," and waft out again, her blue crossover cape wafting with her.

CHAPTER EIGHTEEN

Staincliffe was boring. Even when we were allowed to go for a walk, (which was only on a Sunday), there was no where exciting to go. I was never allowed out on my own either. Meryl, Cynthia and Jean always accompanied me. It would have been less boring on my own. More often than not we just walked along the drab streets in our best clothes, feeling dull as dishwater.

On my second time at Sunday school, I found myself walking once more along the ginnell with the girls towards the sweetshop on the corner of Green Lane. Meryl made us all buy Jubblies – gynormous pyramids of frozen orange, ugh, but it was best not to be different. Jean poked my arm hard,"I heard Auntie Doreen say you're gunner join t'Brownies with us," she said. That sounds like fun, I didn't think. If Brownies were supposed to be kind girls who helped people, what were these girls doing being one.

Outside the sweetshop, fiddling with the wax packets to get them open, Meryl suddenly demanded sixpence off Cynthia and me. "I'm saving up for a tennis racket I've seen in Dewsbury," she said, "An' I 'aven't nearly enough." I handed mine over immediately and she snatched it off me with sticky Jubbly fingers.

"I'm not giving you mine," scowled Cynthia.

"Give me it!" cried Meryl, but Cynthia held back. Suddenly, Meryl's whole face altered; her teeth clamped together, her eyes screwed up behind her huge glasses and she went purple as a berry about to burst. A rumbling started, or was it a growling, as her clenched fists shook and she was no longer Meryl. I backed away. "Gimme it, gimme it, gimme it!" The monster shrieked, till eventually Cynthia handed her sixpence over.

After about four weeks of living in the Cottage Homes, Auntie Flossy allowed me to into town with Meryl, Jean and Cynthia, one Saturday. It was only when we caught the bus into the centre of Dewsbury that I realised whereabouts I was living. We strung along the metal stands of the long bus bays and into town. We'd just been given our two shillings pocket money and everyone was eager to spend it.

Dewsbury was a dreary town with tall chimneys thumping the skyline. Grey mills frowned upon grey buildings and grey streets busy with shoppers. After walking through a little snicket and past a poky place called 'Caddy's Ice Cream Parlour', Cynthia said, "Lets go into Woolworth's, they've loads er sweets in there."

Meryl had a better idea. She stood stock still in the middle of the pavement, huddled us together and said, "When we get in there we'll pinch some."

Pinch some? I couldn't do that. What ever would Nanna think? She had always said that no matter how poor we were we must *never, ever* take anything that didn't belong to us

"An' don't you g' getting' caught." Meryl wagged a finger at me.

"No… no…" I stuttered.

Like a little band of robbers we stole across the road past Jessop's - The 50 bob tailor's, and through the big brass-handled glass doors of Woolworth's. I lagged behind, glancing this way and that.

"Come on," hissed Jean, as they disappeared round the corner past some glasswear. When I finally caught up with them, they were in a tight blob of syrup sniggering at the sweetcounter, sticky fingers at the ready. Meryl saw me, and pulled me in, scowling.

The sweet counter had finger marks on the glass, and the shelves dripped with the promise of Devonshire Toffees, Liquorice Allsorts and chocolate drops for those who could pay for them honestly. The other girls were waiting for the stallholder to turn towards the immense brass scales. I hopped from one foot to the other, like Mammy did, and said a silent prayer to myself – for what I was about to do, may Nanna know I was truly sorry.

Then it happened. I can't remember whose arm went out first, but suddenly I was grabbing, grabbing, grabbing everything I could; Swizzler's, toffee lollipops, chocolate. All were secure in my pocket before I realised what was going on.

"Put them back!" boomed a voice, and Cynthia, Meryl and Jean dropped instantly what was in their hands, and scarpered. I ran after them, skidding on the polished floor banging into the corner of 2/6 stall as we charged tripping over ourselves to pull the heavy doors open.

Outside, there was no time for breath. Across the road past the tailors, the toy shop, the shoe shop, the ice cream parlour, and through the snicket all the way back to the bus-station.

On the bus, no one said anything, except Meryl. As soon as she'd got her breath back her fists clenched, her teeth clamped together, and everyone knew what was coming next.

Once we got off the bus we dashed round the side of Home One.

"Right let's see wat yer've all got," said Meryl, (calmer now) as she dug out her small hoard for us to see. (They hadn't managed to get much before they were caught.) My pockets were full of Swizzlers, Sun Pat Raisins and a bar of Five Boy's Chocolate. I even had a handful of lollipops.

"Yer daft bugger." Meryl eyed them jealously. "Yer not supposed to steal *that* many!"

❧❧

The Brownie threat didn't go away. Auntie Doreen issued me with a washed out brown uniform which reminded me of our old slop bucket, and made me attend silly meetings. During September it was 'bob-a-job' week. As it was supposed to be a good cause, a few of us were allowed home from school a little later than usual. Meryl, who had lived in the Home a long time and had got to know a few of the locals, said she was taking us to see Mrs Greaves. Mrs Greaves apparently lived in a little terraced house on Gladstone Street. I'd rather have gone bob-a-jobbing on my own.

"She always gives us summet t'do for 'bob-a-job." Meryl grinned. "An' sometimes she gives us a biscuit as well."

I tagged along back streets after Meryl and the others, and onto a little lane. When Mrs Greaves opened the door, and I saw how how bent and old she was, I felt much more kindly towards her, and would have eagerly run off to the shop for bread, if Meryl hadn't have dashed off before me. The rest of us went to wait inside, and I felt sorry when I had to leave the tiny, cosy house with its pot sink set in an alcove. The others were just satisfied with their biscuits and Meryl with her bob. I thought of the tennis racket she wanted.

Girls came and girls went. Where to, who knows? Perhaps to another Home, or maybe back to their families.

One Saturday night, two sisters were admitted to Home One. They were shoved in through the living room door kicking and screaming. We were surprised to see them. Their little elfin faces were dirty and tearstained. Their clothes stank. After a quick head inspection, Auntie Flossy declared that the pair of them had lice. Chairs were dragged in the middle of the living room floor, bowls of hot water and towels were fetched from the kitchen, then the poor girls were told to remove their clothing. Despite strong protests they were left standing with nothing on but their knickers, and ringed by giggling girls. Auntie Flossy darted into the store room for the nit comb and a large pair of silver scissors.

"Cum 'ere." She grabbed one of the new arrivals by the arm. "There's only one way to get rid er them nits...now stand still while ah cut your 'air."

The little girl looked horrified. Her eyes already red with tears, now blazed with anger. "Ah'm not 'avin' me 'air cut n' yer can't make me!" She screamed, lashed out with her feet and tried to make a run for it.

"Matron's orders," yelled Flossy. "Cum 'ere Doreen yer'll 'ave to 'elp mi t'hold 'er."

Auntie Doreen, who had just poured some foul smelling liquid into the bowl of warm water, stubbed out her cigarette, shoved it in her apron pocket, and rushed over.

"Now she's in for it," I thought, hardly daring to watch. The spark-man's Wishing Powder would've come in handy now.

The little girl wriggled and fought as best she could, but once in the vice-like grip of the two big strong aunties she had little hope of getting away. Her sister, slightly younger than her, looked on helpless and afraid.

What a sorry sight those two small girls looked minutes later, standing there in little grey knickers, ribs sticking out like a dinosaur fossil and hair that would have been more suited to a convict.

"An' don't think you lot er gettin' away wi it, it's your turn next," grinned Auntie Flossy, looking at the rest of us.

❧❧

Days came and went. Sometimes I'd see Valerie at school, and sometimes I wouldn't. Meal times became a blur of uninteresting food in front of me which was there so long it went cold. Sometimes I felt sick afterwards, and sometimes I didn't. One night in early November, after just such a meal, the phone rang. It was Beech Towers enquiring what I would like for Christmas. Apparently most of the other girls had ordered their present before I arrived. I had a choice of either a wristwatch or a vanity bag. I was just about to say wristwatch, because I didn't know what the heck a vanity bag was, when the other girls shouted "Vanity bag, vanity bag. You must have a vanity bag... we're all having one." I was already in the bad books with the girls after Matron had said to several naughty ones, "Why can't you be good and quiet, like Heather?" So a vanity bag it was.

As Christmas approached, cards began to drop through the letterbox. A tree was stood up on a little table next to the windows and long loops of paper trimmings were unfolded and hung from the ceiling. Auntie Flossy handed me a small white envelope.

"Someone gave me this to give to you," she said.

"What is it?" I asked.

"Open it and see."

I tore open the envelope and found inside a colourful Christmas card. On the front, a little girl wearing a bright red bobble hat and red mittens. She was sitting on a sledge, being pulled by another boy, who was slightly bigger than she was. He was dressed in a dark brown coat, blue hat and matching mittens. The card had been coloured by hand in thick splodges of wax crayon. Inside, untidy writing said:

To Heather
Love from Derek Goodall.

Derek Goodall lived in Home Six. He was tall and dark – a bit like my lost brother Arnold, (except that his hair was curly and Arnold's was straight.) He was the only person in the Homes who was ever kind. Sometimes, if he saw anyone picking on me he would jump over the dividing wall and shove them away and ask if I was O.K. Once he'd asked me to kiss him, but I'd said no. Then some of the other girls had thought it was fun to drag me towards him. I had seen by the look on his face that he'd felt sorry for having made trouble for me and had tried to put things right by telling them he was only kidding and that they had to let me go.

Auntie Flossy said to put the card on top of the television set. Then her and some of the other girls began teasing me about having a boyfriend. I began to wish he'd never sent it. But deep down though, I spent a lot of time admiring it. It was the first Christmas card I had ever received, and the only thing I had here which was mine. I wished the children on the front were Arnold and me, and began to conjure up all kinds of lovely images of a family Christmas – just like Rupert's.

"Auntie Flossy says yer've t'cum wi' uz after school tomorrer," Cynthia suddenly announced after tea one evening. "We've t'rehearse at Methodist Church 'all fer uz concert."

'Uz' meant Cynthia, Jean and Meryl.

Heather Coupland

I'd already had the choice of opting out of the concert, but Auntie Flossy must have thought it would do me good to get out of the Home a bit, and watch rehearsals. Or then again, she might have had other reasons.

When I first set foot through the Church Hall door the following evening, it was like stepping through a magic door instead, straight into the Parachial Hall back in Marsden. The same dusty church hall smell, the same church hall echo as feet clomped across the same church hall woodblock floor. Even a few mothers from the school who'd come to help were scraping the same church hall chairs into place. I plonked down onto one of the chairs and watched Cynthia, Jean and Meryl run round the back of the stage.

I waited, as silence fell. Then someone giggled and was shushed. Out trooped half a dozen girls, Meryl and Jean amongst them, and arranged themselves, smirking, into a horseshoe. The piano struck up some tune I'd never heard before and the girls started singing: "I'm a pink toothbrush, you're a blue toothbrush, have we met somewhere before?"

I almost smiled despite myself. The words were so silly. And Meryl and Jean looked rather silly too, singing as if they really liked the song, bobbing their heads forward all together at various points when some lady at the front did it to prompt them, and doing ridiculous actions throughout. Jean slid and nearly fell on the shiny stage as they shuffled off giggling.

"Quiet please," urged an adult voice. "Group two, on you come."

Several more girls trotted out. I didn't know any, but some might have been from Homes Two or Three, there were that many of us. Again, the prim pianist in the pink cardigan and horn-rimmed glasses set to work. Another tune I didn't know, another urge to almost smile at words which didn't mean anything.

"We've got high hopes," chorused the girls "We've got hi-i-i-igh hopes. High apple pie in the sky hopes."

I too had high hopes, but knew I was doomed to spend Christmas in the Cottage Homes.

"Whoops there goes another rubber tree plant," the girls sang, and did a little dancey thing to finish before trooping off.

Several groups came on and sang, sometimes Cynthia was in among them, sometimes Jean or Meryl was, but only on the final song did all three appear together. Just before they began, Jean pushed Meryl, who giggled and pushed back.

"When you've quite finished," called the voice of the woman in charge. "Right. One, two, three, four..."

And the piano played again, but stopped abruptly when the woman in charge held up her hand.

"That girl on the end. Have you forgotten the words?" The girl on the end nodded. The others tittered. A songsheet was found and everyone started again.

They sang a song called Little Donkey, and this time I didn't want to smile. The tune was sad, and reminded me of horses, and donkeys in Mrs Bilcliffe's field, and Willie Woodward's goats, and my dress with giraffes on that I should have been a reindeer in at my own school concert.

I did like the song, but not the memories.

On the evening of the concert, Auntie Flossy made me go again to watch with Jean, Meryl and Cynthia. We clattered up the ginnell afterwards, to the hulking shadows of the Cottage Homes, lit up like the hospital.

On Christmas Eve we were all given a white pillow slip each and scrap of paper with our names on. The other girls got very excited and quite giddy. Some of them had lived in The Home for a long time and knew exactly what to expect. I couldn't join in though, knowing Nanna's fire might be out. I bet she hadn't even a candle.

On Christmas morning I made it to the lavatory first because everyone else rushed downstairs to see if the sacks were full. Our ten white pillow slips were lined up beneath the windows. Everyone was picking out plastic trumpets, dolls, jigsaws and of course, the vanity bags. Although most of the toys were not wrapped in fancy paper, (I expect there were just too many for the housemother to do this) the majority of them were covered in cellophane. In my sack was the 'vanity bag', a bright yellow trumpet, a crayoning book and a small packet of coloured pencils. I also dug out a beautiful baby doll dressed in a pale pink frock and white hat. It smelt of new plastic and reminded me of a ball I had once bought from Moorhouse's. In the bottom of the sack was a jigsaw puzzle, with a picture of some puppies on the lid, and best of all a Dean book of Bible Stories. I was just about to sit down and read it when Jean Livesey zoomed across. "I'll 'ave that." She snatched it from me. "An' you can 'ave this." She thrust a small packet of Plasticine Modelling Clay into now empty hands, "It should 'ave been in my sack anyway!"

She whizzed back to her little patch of carpet and plonked herself down. There she sat for a good half an hour flicking through my pages. From the corner of my eye she looked like a mean little goblin. I began to wish that Rupert and Bill Badger would appear and whisk the unpleasant Pine Ogress to some far away land.

After breakfast Auntie Doreen said we must all help to clear up the mess of coloured paper, cardboard and cellophane, which was as deep as our rag pile at home. Our television had broken down the night before, so Home Two had agreed to lend us theirs, so we could watch the Chipperfield's Christmas Circus and Billy Cotton's Christmas Party.

"But only fer th' afternoon," blustered Auntie Flossy who wore a dress which looked like a cushion cover. "An' mind you all say thank you to Auntie Hilda when she brings it in."

At about one o'clock Auntie Flossy announced that the Christmas dinner was on its way over from Beech Towers. The girls cheered. Out of the window I saw a porter rattling a wonky-wheeled trolley across the tarmac. Ten minutes later, large tureens were set upon the table, stuffing and apple sauce were placed at either end and beside each child's place was a Christmas cracker.

"Yer can cum n' sit down now," called Auntie Flossy. "But don't start pulling them there crackers until I say so."

There was the usual grumble of 'awww', but Auntie Flossy was adamant. It wasn't until we were all seated quietly at the table that she said, "Right yer can pull em now." I pulled my cracker with Yvonne. It didn't crack, exactly, just made a dull paper-tearing sound and out fell a little plastic dog and a paper hat. Yvonne made a grab for the hat and stuck it on her head – which was the best place for it. She let me have the dog. During the effort of pulling the cracker, I had fallen back into Jean Burrhouse on my other side, who was loads bigger than everyone else.

"Watch it, skinny, " she snorted, pushing me back.

Then, in came Matron. The Aunties snapped to attention. "Hello girls. I wish you all a happy Christmas, and I hope you're all behaving yourselves."

The Christmas feast in front of us would have been a miracle on the table at Millstone Cottages, but it had been prepared with hospital sterility a million miles from Marsden. I wondered if Arnold was eating up, wherever he was. Auntie Flossy poked me in the back, "Stop playing with them sprouts, Heather," she said, just as Maureen discovered the sixpence in her portion of pudding.

CHAPTER NINETEEN

Whilst out walking with a group of the other girls, (We were meant to be running an errand to the hospital, but had strayed a little and ended up in the grounds of Jean Burrhouse's school) I noticed a border of bright daffodils growing beneath the windows. Their frilly golden trumpets blew a stiff, silent tune in the breeze. The sight of this sudden spectacular yellowness rattled some coals deep within me. My spirits lifted and the all the apathy of life in the Cottage Homes disappeared. Just for a moment, as I wandered through countryside unrestricted by Housemothers and bedtimes, I skipped, in my head, along little lanes, stopping to peep at the beautiful petals of the primroses and pink purslane that hid in the hedges, gazing an instant at the rose coloured buds of tall sycamores.

"'urry up 'eather." I was dragged back to the school gate, with a final glance at the daffodils, and trailed back to the Cottage Homes, some way behind the others.

Auntie Elsie (Flossy was away for Easter) was in a bad mood. *Someone* had already eaten some of their Easter egg. (The eggs, each in a little box with a picture of two baby lambs frolicking around in a patch of green grass, were kept in the store room at the back of the house. They were not meant to be touched until Easter Sunday – it was only Saturday.) That *somebody* was in serious trouble. Would they like to admit it now before their identity was revealed?

No one spoke: but I knew that now I was in real trouble. A few days earlier I had seen Jean Livesey and Meryl poking around in the storeroom, taking the smarties out of *my* egg and secreting them in *their* pocket.

"Don't you dare say owt." Meryl had dug me in the ribs when she'd spotted me watching them.

"Right then," snarled Auntie Elsie. "Seein' as the culprit's not goin' t'own up ah'll tell yer who it is. Follow me."

Like a pack of little lap dogs, Jean Livesey, Yvonne, Margaret, Jane, and lastly, me (the remaining six girls were no where to be seen) followed Auntie Hell-sie across the carpet and into the store room. Everyone crowded round and waited anxiously as the hated hand of Auntie Elsie reached up and slowly plucked one of the chocolate eggs from its perch.

The purple foil in which it was wrapped was slightly crumpled. They hadn't even bothered to hide the fact that it had been tampered with. Waving the little green box in front of our noses, Elsie growled, "Now shall I open the lid and see whose name is inside? Or are *we* goin' t'own up?"

If I told the truth, Jean would bash me half to death, and Meryl would have one of her fist-shaking fits and finish me off. If I said nothing, Auntie Elsie would do the job for them.

"Right then…" she rasped, in a voice as coarse as a scouring stone, "Lets see who it is."

Flap by flap she began pulling apart the little lid of the chocolate egg, (it was like watching her pull the stumpy wings off chicks) needling her finger under each cardboard fold, which gave way with a r…i…i…ippp. She stabbed at the name.

"It's Heather," said Yvonne relieved, staring at the blue ink.

"Heather! Yes, Heather! Now would you like to explain to me *why* it says Heather an' why you didn't own up when you had the chance!"

My life flashed before me. There was nothing to say.

"Go n' fetch yer Brownie belt" she hissed "Ah'll show yer what yer get for being so deceitful."

I sloped into the clothing closet, very slowly removed the thin leather belt attached to my little brown dress, and sloped back, wilting under the heat of eyes. Auntie Elsie began lashing me with the leather strap. Blow after blow stung the backs of my legs.

"Now get up them stairs n' cum down until I say so."

I held my head up, forcing the tears back, knowing each whack wasn't really for me, but for Jean, and Meryl and the others. I caught sight of Auntie Elsie's face in the mirror. It was twisted into an evil sneer.

"An' pull t'curtains on," she shouted up to me as I limped into the dormitory -
"Both lots!"

Outside I could hear the hum of the other girls' voices. It served them right to
have only a yard with swings to play in, when I had an entire moor.

Even the following morning my punishment was not allowed to stop. Whilst
all the other children munched on their eggs, I was ordered to clean out the grate
in Auntie Flossy's bedroom, ready for her return. "Red legs, red legs," rang in my
ears as I trailed upstairs with the ash bucket and shovel.

"That'll teach you t'be deceitful," prickled Auntie Elsie again.

Auntie Flossy's bedroom was not anything like the dormitories and it smelt of
a perfumy Auntie Flossy smell. It was large and square with a big double bed
which had a flowered quilt cover thrown over it. (It seemed strange to see a room
with only *one* bed.) On the wall opposite the window was a dressing table with a
letter on it, addressed to Florence, so that was her real name, I'd never thought she
looked like a Flossy, she was too thin and sharp. In front of the letter were
various cosmetics like miniature versions of the tall buildings in Dewsbury and
Huddersfield. One of the buildings was a square roofed bottle of scent as long
and narrow as Auntie Flossy herself. So that's the smell, I thought, checking out
its name – Primitif by Max Factor in a vicious red flame up the middle, around
dreary yellow scent; the same colour as Auntie Flossy's nails. A horrible name,
with a horrible smell. Remembering why I was in here, I knelt down at the black
cast iron fireplace, and started to fettle.[*]

৵৽

It wasn't long after Jean Livesey had gone (she'd suddenly just left one day –
transferred, Auntie Doreen had said) that I noticed Meryl, Cynthia and about five
others in a lump, at the back of Home One whispering, giggling and sometimes
glancing at me. I stayed away, but every time I checked to see what they were up
to, they were still folded together, like a book I'd seen Auntie Flossy shift around
sometimes, but never open.

After a bit, each page fell away from the spine of girls and ran to where I was
sitting, plucking out blades of grass.

"Hello skinny," growled Meryl. I said nothing. There were a few titters. I
pulled out the grass harder, pretending it was Meryl's hair.

"You're comin' with us, down the field."

I stood straight up. Going with the group down the field wasn't a good idea,

---

[*] *Clean.*

but to say no was even worse, so I let myself be pushed and dragged and herded along to a quiet place where they penned me in, each girl a fencepost in her dumpy outdoor shoes.

"Heather's simple," said one of them. "She dun't know owt."

"Yeah," grinned another, "a right dunce."

"'ow d'yer spell 'Liquorice', dunce?"

I spelt it out the best way I could, but Meryl cackled in my face, and jabbed me in the shoulder. Everyone else started laughing. I turned round, glancing from one to the next, each eye cold and hard, reflecting me twice, four times, a dozen times; tiny, useless, weak.

Sometimes one to them would push me so hard, I fell back into someone else, who shoved me away. Back and forth, I was bait and they were crows.

"Go on Meryl," one girl squawked, "ask her another."

"What's 'eavier, a ton er coal or a ton er feathers?" Whose best, Cliff Richard or Elvis? How much is 275 times 13?" Poke, prod, jab… "Skinny."

"Softie."

"Simple."

"Dunce."

"Skinny, softie, simple, dunce. Skinny, softie, simple, dunce…"

For each question I got wrong, I got a handful of something flung in my face; grass sometimes, or bits of paper from Meryl's pocket.

"'ow many legs has a spider got?" Someone else shouted.

"Eight." I whimpered. They couldn't do me for getting that right, and there was a pause, then,

"Wrong." Small pebbles hit me in the face, and the girls showered me with hateful laughter.

"Spiders have six legs, stupid. They're insects. Don't yer know nothing?" mocked Meryl, and again the chant rose like a wave round me.

"Skinny, softie, simple, dunce. Skinny, softie, simple, dunce." I let them get a few more pushes in, and imagined how foolish they'd look in lessons if they were asked how many legs a spider had. Meryl had caught one the other day, she should have counted its legs while she was pulling them out. But I didn't say that, I didn't say anything, only answers to stupid questions which were all wrong.

It was a public flogging. I thought back to the stocks in Marsden, where folk had been locked and had everyone in the village come to snigger and sling rotten fruit at them.

"There's Matron, scarper," said someone, and I was alone again, with bits of paper and small stones round my feet where they'd landed.

CHAPTER TWENTY

Daffodils died, and out came the spun rayon skirts, Bry-nylon cardigans and summer knickers. I was still not used to their staticky crackles when something else happened to make my skin prickle. Mammy turned up. I hadn't heard anything from her (or anyone else come to that), since leaving Millstone Cottage. If I had thought for one minute that she had come to take me back I would have been overjoyed to see her, but no one left the Homes *that* easy. When Auntie Flossy showed her into the living room, I knew my questions about Nanna, Graham and Arnold would never get answered.

"Ah've brought yer some picture books," said Mammy, sitting herself down and yanking open the zip of her shopping bag.

Books! My ears pricked up. So too did the ears of all the other girls who had gathered around for a nosy.

"Ere yer are," she passed me a brown paper bag. It was crumpled around the top and had 'W. H. Smith's' splashed across the middle in blue writing. I would have loved to save the surprise for later, steal away somewhere quiet and open the bag slowly, but Mammy would have thought it very bad manners, and the other girls would have insisted that I open it.

I was hoping the parcel was a Rupert book, a Girls Crystal or even a Bunty. It was neither. The other girls, Pat, Margaret and Jane all burst out laughing.

"Teddy Tales," they all giggled. "An' Jack n' Jill of Buttercup Farm. Ahhh… ahhh…a… ah… ahhh… Baby."

"Only babies read books like that," said Jane smugly.

Mammy's face went as black as the grate I'd cleaned in Auntie Flossy's room on Easter Sunday. "Well, you like them, don't you Heather?" If I said yes, the other girls would tease me. If I said no, Mammy would be upset. In the end I just laughed. A little pretend laugh, a nervous laugh. Mammy was mortified. She jumped out of the chair, grabbed her bag and marched towards the outside door, slamming it shut behind her. Auntie Flossy, who had been preparing the tea, peeped her head around the door.

"What were all that about?"

I just shrugged my shoulders and felt sad.

It didn't take me long to realise I had made a huge mistake. How was Mammy to know the books were babyish? She couldn't read the titles. It had probably taken quite a lot of guts for her to actually get here. Reading the destination on the front of a bus was quite beyond her, and having to keep asking people the way would be flummoxing. Why hadn't I told the other girls to push off and mind their own business?

Leaving the two books on the chair by the table (I had neither the heart nor the courage to read them), I went outside and mooched about the grounds. I hadn't been out long when Auntie Doreen shouted of me. "Your mother's on the phone, Heather."

I'd never spoken on the telephone before. The closest I'd ever come was one time when Mammy had dragged me into the little red telephone box opposite the Post Office in Marsden. She been trying to leave a garbled message to the County Court in Huddersfield – something to do with 'Wainwright n' 'is maintinunce money'. But not knowing which button to press - A or B - she had got in a bit of a mess. Fortunately for her, but not for me, I'd happened to be walking past at that time - so she'd dived outside, grabbed me by my coat sleeve and pulled me in.

"Press one er these bloody buttons fer me," she'd said. I'd pressed one of the 'bloody buttons' and Mammy was able to make her call.

Auntie Flossy was standing beside the big black telephone with a length of cord dangling over one finger. She passed me the receiver. There was no button to press.

"Ello." I whispered.

A torrent of abuse swilled into my ear as Mammy played hell with me for a good ten minutes.

"That's last time I'm h'ever comin' t'see you yer ungrateful little bugger. Ah cum all this way n' wat do ah get but sniggers, nowt but bloody sniggers. Well, ah can tell yer now ah'm vexed. Very vexed!"

If she said 'vexed' once she must have said it fifty times. No matter how much I tried to butt in and say I was sorry, Mammy kept yelling... 'vexed, vexed, vexed!' Then the receiver went dead. Even after I placed it back on the hook, that horrible word kept ringing in my ears. The two Aunties stood with their arms folded, Auntie Doreen's cigarette pluming like Bankbottom chimney.

"Bit cross was she?" asked Auntie Flossy.

I crossed the room and when I got to the door I turned around, the Aunties were dancing to Saturday Club on the wireless, like they did every weekend.

Sitting alone on the dry grass, the more I thought about home the worse I felt. If I darted up the steps and through the gate perhaps I could run along the ginnel and catch a bus into Dewsbury before anyone missed me. My two shillings pocket money pressed against me, safe inside my pocket. If I couldn't afford th'up bus it wouldn't have mattered. As long as I could dance along my canal bank and skip up my lanes. At this time of year the hedgerows would be a mass of wild flowers and the thick gorse growing alongside the railway embankment, golden-yellow. On such a fine day the sun would be dappling through the treetops, casting shadows onto the fields below. I could almost hear the flap of a bird wing as I ran up Boat Lane and smell the sweet familiar scent of willow and wood smoke. Even the dusty road belonged to me.

Nanna would stare up from the lumpy tickin in astonishment as I burst through the door, and it being Saturday, Graham would have been into town and brought some Battenburg back for tea. It seemed years since I'd sunk my teeth into the marzipan surrounding Graham's Battenburg. I could never enjoy cake in the Homes.

"Tea's ready!"

The rough voice bellowing from the doorstep startled me from my real, but imaginary food. For a moment I was suspended between my home and The Home. A sudden clout on the back of my head reminded me of where I was. Jean Burrhouse ran past laughing. Auntie Flossy had seen her, but said nothing. Already, some of the other girls from Home One were making their way up the drive. To make a dash for it now would be silly. I remembered what had happened to Theresa and Maria, from Home Three, who'd made off as far as Oldham. If I got caught I might be beaten black and blue with a leather belt, and get my name on the wireless. With this in mind, I scrambled up and dragged myself indoors.

The kitchen doorway was crammed with girls bending down to swap their sturdy lace up shoes for crepe-soled sandals. I followed the same dull ritual and trailed behind them into the living room.

Somebody, probably Auntie Flossy, had pushed the huge oak table away from its usual place by the window, and into the middle of the floor. Instead of the normal place settings, were a stack of plates and two piles of sandwiches. Ten white beakers rose up in neat rows. In the centre of the table stood the tall pot milk jug and sugar basin. Both benches had been placed next to the table. It all looked like a picture I'd seen of a new power station.

"What's in t'sandwiches?" asked Yvonne as she sidled up to the table for a sneaky look.

"Brawn!" Yelled Auntie Flossy from the kitchen.

"Brawn? What's that supposed t'be?"

"Potted meat." Her voice drew nearer as she emerged from the kitchen with the big chrome teapot in both hands. "An' before any of yer starts, just let me remind yer if yer don't eat six pieces each yer'll be sittin' at t'table 'til midnight!"

The knot in my stomach tightened.

Jean Burrhouse and Pat were already sitting down. They had appetites like elephants. The rest of us trailed into the wash room. Soon the six little white sinks were bubbling with cold water (hot water was for 'strip wash') and the usual smell of carbolic filled the room. As I swilled my hands I thought of Mammy. She was certainly very vexed. Vexed enough to keep me in the Home forever. I unhooked a towel from a peg on the wall but Yvonne snatched it from me.

"Sit down for crying out loud!" Auntie Flossy's eyes were pinpricks as I dithered around trying to find somewhere to sit. Like a well-trained circus animal, I sat immediately – on the edge of the bench right next to her. Jean and Pat were sitting opposite and I could see them with their hands over their mouths, stifling laughter.

"Why we always have t'have this palaver with you I just don't know!" Auntie Flossy continued. "Get six squares. Six squares ah said not four, not five – six!"

Just then, after anxiously glancing out of the window, she called into the kitchen, "Put that fag out Doreen, Matron's on her rounds," and in Matron stalked in her navy skirt and red-braided cape.

"I hope you're all behaving yourselves, girls," she said.

"Yes Matron," everyone chorused. And off she clomped to ask Home Two the same question.

Amid the usual hum that accompanied meal times, I struggled with the gristly meat paste sandwiches like I struggled with everything. The first mouthful alone made me want to gip. Everyone else went to put their shoes back on and were long gone. I was still sitting there with the spectre of Auntie Bossy hanging over me to make sure I ate every last crumb. By the time I had finally got it all down it was nearly six thirty.

"Go n' wash yer plate n' yer pot," she groaned from behind a 'Woman's Own'.

As dusk began to fall in the large dormitory later that evening, I was still thinking of Mammy. So too were Barbara and Jane, whispering on Jane's bed. "You don't call yer mum Mammy do yer?" They giggled. "Yer big baby, calling yer mum Mammy and reading baby books Mammy got yer. Wait till we tell Jean." The other five beds stood empty – like big black coffins waiting to be filled. Jean Burrhouse would be bounding in soon, with Pat, who'd be talking loudly about boys, and kissing, and babies again. And after tonight would be tomorrow – Sunday, and Meryl would be tormenting me on the way to church, in the church and on the way back from church. There was no way of escaping. And whatever was I going to call Mammy? 'Mammy' was too babyish, 'Mother' too old fashioned, and 'Mum' too caring. 'Wainwright' was Wainwright, I couldn't call her 'Topczewski', because that was the Goblin, so I'd call her nothing. It was all blurring into one dark mess, a tunnel with the holes closing, worrying about Mammy, Meryl and Jean, one minute and the next listening in horror as someone, somewhere began screaming for help. Loud and piercing, it ripped through my ears, a lumberjack's saw... and it was getting louder. Terrified, I sat bolt upright in bed, banging my head loudly on the tubular metal frame. The yelling stopped. So too did Barbara and Jane's whispering.

"Wat the 'ell's up wi 'er?" Asked Jane in a loud voice. "She frightened me t' death."

"Wat the 'ell are yer doin' yer daft sod?"

"Ah want light on," I squeaked, rubbing my sore head.

"Ah want light on," mocked Barbara.

"Well yer know t'rules, yer can't 'ave light on, so shurrup n' go t'sleep?"

They began tittering. Afraid of the scream starting again, I slipped beneath the newly laundered sheets. They smothered me.

"Help! Help!" The spine chilling voice began again. I buried by head deeper into the pillow, but even with my fingers stuck in my ears, the crying continued. Suddenly, from somewhere, I saw a terrified little girl. She was cowering in a corner at the bottom of the field. The shadow of a man in a flat cap and a raincoat hovered above her. In an attempt to defend herself, the petrified child raised a skinny arm against him. The man drew nearer... it was dark and she was alone... there was no one to protect her. He was going to murder her... "No...! No!" I trembled.

The next thing I knew someone was standing beside my bed pulling the covers from over my head. It was Jane.

"Wat the bloody 'ell do yer keep whining for?"

Unable to answer I continued to whimper.

"Go n' fetch Auntie Flossy," Jane called to Barbara. "There's summet up wi' 'er but she won't tell me what."

There was a patter of bare feet crossing the oilcloth, and opening and shutting of doors. Within minutes Barbara had returned with Auntie Flossy.

"Wat's up? Why do yer keep cryin'?" She asked. Again I couldn't answer. I could not explain to her how unhappy I was feeling. Instead I lay still, curled up like a little hedgehog. Auntie Flossy flopped onto the bed beside me. She began unfolding my arms, which I had coiled tightly around my head.

"Now tell me wat's upsetting yer."

Between short, deep beaths, I began to tell her of the little girl at the bottom of the field. "She was shoutin' fer 'elp."

Auntie Flossy listened, shrugging bony shoulders. "There's nubdi been cryin'," she insisted." We'd 'ave 'erd em. You must have been dreaming. Now forget all about it n' go t'sleep."

The voices disappeared, but the echoes of them hung round in my head and snared me when I least expected it. One day at school, I heard that Mammy had visited but had not been allowed to see me. An older girl had seen her going into the headmaster's office, had heard the rumpus that followed, and excitedly described to me all the horrible things Mammy had been shouting.

What did she want? Was she still vexed with me? Maybe I could have said sorry. What if it had nowt to do with vexed? What if Nanna had died and Mammy had come to tell me. Horrible images flamed inside my head, and continued to flame as I stumbled across the playground into the dining room. Collapsing into my seat, the trembling started. It lasted throughout grace, throughout the queue at the counter, and all throughout dinner. My knife and fork shook together, clumsily attempting to pick through cabbage and cold meat which were warmer than I was. My food somehow reached my mouth, and was trampled between teeth I wasn't controlling.

"Are you alright?" A dinner lady was suddenly at my side.

"Yes." I stammered.

Then she left me. I could see her out of the corner of my eye heading towards the table of tureens.

"Please, please don't go," I wanted to cry, "please come back and tell me why Mammy came."

But it was too late. There'd be no kind words, no warm blanket of sympathy, just a fork juddering against a plate, then a spoon struggling with jelly.

That afternoon, on the way home from school I blurted out my fears to Yvonne. As soon as we got back to the Homes Yvonne blabbed. Auntie Flossy strode over with a look on her face of things to come. "Yer daft beggar, whatever put that thought in your silly head. 'ere, forget about it an' tek yer sandals to t'cobblers* to 'ave that buckle sewn back on."

After a couple of weeks with no more news of Mammy, the whole school was given a day off from lessons in honour of Princess Margaret's 'fairy tale' wedding to Mr Antony Armstrong-Jones, whoever they were.

"One squeak out er any on yer today...n' yer'll know about it." Hmphed Auntie Doreen. "Me n' Auntie Flossy's watching t'wedding all day'. And they did. The television went on at dawn and didn't go off until the last piece of confetti had fluttered down the Mall and across our screen.

Most of us caught occasional glimpses of black and white figures in black and white costumes, and black and white hands waving stiffly from black and white carriages. Princess Margaret, it appeared, was 'the most beautiful bride'.

---

* *The cobbler's was round the side of Beech Towers. It was like a blacksmith's forge, but without a furnace. It always smelt of warm leather. The cobbler was a friendly, homely little man who was surrounded by buckles, laces and lumps of leather, and always seemed to have a Last in his hand.*

Someone pointed out Princess Anne, who I knew already because Nanna once said she was the same age as me. She was a lucky little girl because she had her own pony. I'd seen pictures of her in the Huddersfield Examiner.

With the distraction of the boring all-day wedding, meals were a bit any-old-how, nobody at all noticed that I was only pretending to eat.

I knew no good would have come from watching that cowboy film one Saturday afternoon, when the most beautiful bride and her black and white husband were no doubt getting on with their colourful lives, and were no longer being glorified by the housemothers. When we were outside, I saw that familiar huddle behind Home One, but what followed was a different variation of their 'Get Heather' game.

The Question Game had become boring to them. They were struggling to think of questions, and were even asking ones they'd asked before. This time I could see them galloping towards me, and as usual let myself be captured.

"We're stakin' you out, softie," howled Meryl, as they bundled me down to their favourite corner and ordered me to lie down on the grass. I did as I was told.

"We're gunner crozzle yer in t'midday sun," said one of the others.

"Crozzle yer good," added another.

"Tek yer socks off so we can tie yer down to these sticks and stretch yer out," ordered Meryl, and around her the girls leapt like flames. I pulled off my socks, frightened to do otherwise, and Meryl pulled them tight round my wrists.

"We'll need some more t'tie 'er legs up wi'. "Meryl glanced from one girl to the next. "Cynthia, yours'll do."

Cynthia said nothing as she handed her socks over. Meryl snatched them, and set to work, a sneer on her face.

"An' don't you move," she threatened "er else we'll pour water on yer bed an' sey you wet yerself."

From the distance, a voice called. Time to go in. The Indians stopped their whooping, and ran up the field. Meryl kicked my foot as she passed.

"Yer'll crozzle in about an hour," and she cantered off.

I could have easily pulled apart my ropes, but I thought of the wet bed, and stayed put for a while, crozzling.

CHAPTER TWENTY-ONE

I was on my way to school one morning in June with Meryl and Cynthia. Meryl was still on about that tennis racket Cynthia and me must have paid for several times over, and Meryl still hadn't got. I tried to imagine her wobbling along in badly fitting shorts after balls she couldn't hit, and having one of her fits each time she missed. We had just come through the big iron gates and walked a little way along the road when my thoughts were startled from me by a short witchy figure that swept out at us from behind a wall, shrieking. "Cum on, 'eather, yer comin' 'ome wi me!"

My jaw dropped to the floor.

"An' if you two promise not to tell anybody ah'll... ah'll send yer five shillin' h'each... through t'post," added the woman I used to call Mammy. Meryl and Cynthia's eyes widened with delight.

"We won't tell nubdy, 'eather's mum. Honest," said Meryl.

Well, no one in their right mind was going to turn down the offer of a whole five shillings when gifts at the Home were so rare. For the first time in a long number of months, I actually smiled.

Meryl bared her teeth in wild excitement and shook her fists more violently than I had ever seen her shake them before. As the woman I used to call Mammy and I fled along the pavement, I glanced back and could see that Meryl and Cynthia were staring at us in disbelief. How long would it be though, I wondered, before one of them told somebody. Long enough, perhaps, for us to catch the bus into Dewsbury and be well on our way back home.

"'erry up 'eather," puffed the raven haired gnome in the plimsoles. "H'I saw a bus stop h'over there. H'or was it h'over there by that pub. There's a bus stop h'over 'ere somewhere." She stopped and glanced round, catching her breath.

"There's a pub!" I pointed further up and once again the child stealer was at a gallop, gasping out broken words, "Them buggers at welfare doin' as they liked. Well h'am doin' as h'I like an' h'if they don't like that I'll bloody knife the buggers." It wasn't the pub she'd meant. We dashed on.

At the end of the road by the sweet shop the woman I used to call Mammy veered left and we hurried into an area of red brick council houses and scruffy gardens. I'd never been this way before and hoped she knew where she was going. I'd never seen her running before, she was like a clumsy spider with arms and legs propelling wildly. After trundling a good way along the road, well out of sight of any would be 'tell-tales', we stopped beside a pub called 'The Belle View'.

But there was no bus stop near that pub either. I kept looking back, expecting a welfare worker, a policeman, or worse still, a gang of burly Housemothers striding after us. But there was no-one, not even the A.A. man on his motorcycle.

"We should be h'able t'catch a bus 'ere. H'ah knew it were near a pub," said the woman I'd called Mammy, when we finally spotted the bus stop, and pub she'd meant. "but we'll 'ide behind this 'ere bush til one cums... we don't want h'anybody seein' us, do we?" She dragged me towards an untidy hedge. "Keep lookin' h'out fer a bus 'at seys Dewsbury on it," she continued, peeping out at intervals and peering up the road. She looked worried and began shifting from one foot, to the other. She wasn't the only one who was worried; any minute she might change her mind, or someone from the Homes might come and catch us and drag me back there.

Eventually, a red spot appeared, and grew into the shape and size of a double decker bus. I leapt out from behind the bush.

"This'll do," I cheered. "It seys Dewsbury on t'front."

Throughout the journey we shrank into our seats whenever we spotted groups of girls and boys through the mucky window. They were making their way to school. There was Derek Goodall, who might just miss me, and further on Jean Burrhouse. I grinned at the back of her head, and crouched as we passed.

Once in Dewsbury we flew along narrow rows of metal stands, all the time looking out for people that might tell-on-us. What we needed to find now was a bus that said 'Huddersfield' on the front. In the end my Mother spotted a conductor who was just about to jump on one going to somewhere long with a H on the front.

"H'is this bus goin' t' 'Uddersfield?" She asked him.

"No, Heckmondwike. But if yer 'ang on five minutes t'next 'un is."

These five minutes were like hours. But eventually our bus turned up and we both jumped on. We hid away on the back seat like escaped convicts dodging the law, and bumped around for three-quarters of an hour round dull, unfamiliar streets, past houses, shops, pubs my mother didn't know, through villages. I never spoke and she asked me no questions. At one point, I noticed a police patrol car following us, and huddled more into the corner. I suppose I'd be hunted now for the rest of my life, and would have to hide out on Marsden moor. It was exciting to know I'd see that soon, and Nanna and Graham. We jolted to a halt at some

bus stop, and the police car slid past, then turned up a side street and away. Maybe to catch real criminals. We finally pulled into Huddersfield bus station and juddered to a standstill. I sighed heavily and we got off.

"We'll go in t'a café in t'Top Market fer summet t'eat," said the woman I should still call Mammy. Birds were singing and the sun shone warmer than Beech Towers blankets as we strolled along Upperhead Row and into New Street. Huddersfield was far nicer than Dewsbury, and my mother was the strangest of all. She wasn't swearing, and not a vexed to be heard, maybe I should enjoy my Mammy before she changed.

Down the busy main street, traffic along Buxton Road heaved. One van delivered bread, another groceries. Faded awnings shaded shop windows from bright sunlight. We were dazzled by modern stilettos in Stylo, Timpsons and Freeman, Hardy and Willis. Opposite the shoe shops stood the Curzon Cinema, emblazoned with advertisements and exciting billings showing 'Princess Margaret's Wedding In Springtime' and John Wayne and William Holden in 'Horse Soldiers'.

The Market Hall, when we finally got there, was a seaweed of swaying arms, legs and shopping bags. Coloured hats bobbed along, or darted fishlike past butchers, fishmongers and greengrocery stalls. Little sweet shops with poky windows displayed boxes of Black magic and Dairy Milk. We stopped at one, and my mother unexpectedly gave me a sixpence. My mouth watered over tins of toffees and 'Gypsy Kisses'. Yorkshire Mixtures, with their assortment of sugar coated fishes, mint humbugs and pear drops, stood in tall glass jars, and there were enough raspberry flavoured Arrowbars at 1d each, sherbert lemons, love hearts and swizzlers to keep a dentist busy. After some umming and aahing, I settled for a thrupenny lucky bag and a packet of Spangles. The lucky bag revealed a few dolly sweets and a green plastic 'engagement' ring, which I slipped proudly onto the third finger of my left hand.

My mother bought half a pound of fig biscuits from Emma Eastwoods somewhere in the middle of the market and a pound of mixed Peak Freans. They were displayed in glass-topped tins with the name written in green lettering. In a corner by Howarth the Fruiterers we passed a large sign boasting 'Doctor Dan's Medicinal Drink'. Everyone seemed in need of a little pick-me-up and were queuing by the counter to buy a thrupenny tumbler full.

"Can ah av'e a drink er that stuff?" I asked.

"No, yer don't want any er that. It reminds me er Owd Mother Oram," (my other grandma.) "She drinks buckets full er the bloody stuff." She didn't really, Nanna once told me she drank liquorice.

"We'll go on t'balcony... there's a little place there where we can get an 'am sandwidge n' a nice bun," she added, and we wove our way through a patchwork of hats and shopping baskets to one of the wide staircases, and climbed up to the balcony. This 'little place' turned out to be Murgatroyd's Café. It was lovely, with square tables and a small counter. On the top of the counter was a glass case brimming with apple turnovers, cream horns and sticky buns. Kitty ordered us a cup of tea each, a boiled ham sandwich and a vanilla slice. For the first time in months I was hungry, and gobbled my food in case it disappeared in a dream.

After eating the meal, Kitty had another surprise in store. "We're goin' t' Woolworth's, ah'm gunner buy yer a new dress."

I had *never* in my whole life had a *new* dress!

Back down the stairs I slipped, past Rangeley's Milliners and a man examining nails at an ironmongers with a sign which said 'Fred W. Hindle' and outside, dodging the shopping bags, to Woolworth's.

Woolworths was one of the cheapest shops in town. We made our way through the busy store to where shelves were piled high with skirts, slacks and matching sun tops in bright coloured sail cloth and light cotton. There were Tricel blouses and Orlon cardigans that would apparently 'drip dry', printed dresses with beautiful floral patterns and fashionable trews. Kitty dragged me to the rail that had frocks on.

"We'll get one er these," she said, flicking through the wooden hangers. "They're only 9/11d. Which d'yer like?"

After much backwardsing and forwardsing I chose a pink and white striped one with blue flowers and little leaves. It had a little 'Peter Pan' collar, puffed sleeves and a thin white plastic belt.

One of the assistants folded the dress up into a neat parcel and passed it to me over the big oak counter.

"It should suit you," she beamed. I smiled back.

"H'ah've still a bit left so yer can have a toy if yer want," said Kitty.

After tumbling downstairs into the basement I picked a bright rubber ball with blue and yellow spots on. I strode out of Woolworths proud with my parcels, all bought and paid for.

Kitty shoved me into some public lavatories nearby, "Tek that bloody gymslip off and put yer lovely new frock on." I went into the toilets as just another kid from the Cottage Homes, and came out as Heather.

"We'll go n' catch Marsden bus now," Kitty said. "There's one due h'anytime."

It seemed more exposed in the bus station, more dangerous. It was still not too late for Bossy Bruce or Tweedy Newton to turn up. Glancing this way and that, I followed Kitty onto the Marsden bus. The nearer home we got, the safer I felt, till I stepped onto the kerb on Manchester Road and met the wintry glare of Miss Newton.

Kitty must have reckoned her best form of defense was attack and began screeching at her. I shrunk back, my first glimpse of familiar faces shrunk back with me as they passed us, pretending nothing was up.

"Yer bloody bastards," Kitty's little black eyes flashed in fury, "Tekin' my daughter t' that stinkin' 'ome where there were nowt but bloody bullies! Don't think yer tekin' 'er back there cos yer not! She's stoppin' wi' me! Wi me do yer 'ear? Wi me!"

Miss Newton, calm and controlled, said, "Mrs Topczewski. If I remember rightly it was YOU who requested that Heather be taken into care. It was YOU who rang us and demanded that we take her as soon as possible."

So I was right after all. She *had* been up to summet that sunny day in October. I felt as if I had been hit on the head with a lump hammer. I clutched my parcels pretending not to hear.

"Well she's not goin' back... n' that's that," sniffed Kitty.

"We at the Welfare will decide that," declared Miss Newton in a haughty voice. "And no one else." She turned on her heels and marched off.

"Stupid bitch," muttered Kitty.

After all the excitement of tea in the market, my new dress and ball, I felt deflated. I had visions of Miss Newton marching off to the Police Station and demanding that they send a Black Maria to pick us up.

"Will they cum n' get us?" I trembled.

"Let em try," Kitty snorted. "An' ah'll knife em…ah will… ah knife em."

Kitty had no sooner shoved that knife in when th'up bus rattled along, and we jumped on. I soon put Miss Newton out of my mind when I gazed out of the window at little gardens full of roses, rhododendrens and redhot pokers. Fields bright with buttercups. Newborn lambs skipped about in the long grass and as the little bus approached Private Road End I could see that the trees along Manchester Road were full of leaves.

The bus pulled up beside the grass verge without waiting I was down the steps and across the road. Heather was back in her own little world again.

The air was all new mown hay and hot tar. My feet hardly touched the steps as I darted up them, two at a time. Flinging open the door I stood a moment, taking everything in; the horsehair couch, the old sideboard, Nanna in her bed. I dropped my parcels and ran to her. She was propped up, staring at me as if I was Kathleen returned.

"'eather, 'eather," she squeaked. "'ow 'ave you got 'ere?" She pulled herself up onto bony elbows, reached a gnarled hand out for mine.

"Mi mammy's brought me. An' guess wat… ah'm stoppin'… ah'm not goin' back!"

"Cum 'ere, love," she pulled me towards her. "Ah thought ah'd niver see yer agen. Oh, cum 'ere love… cum 'ere."

"Don't cry, Nanna," I said. "Ah've cum 'ome… n' ah'm not goin' back, ah'm ah?" I turned to Kitty who'd just bounced all pink through the door.

"No yer bloody well h'aren't. Not h'over my dead body!" She dropped the brown paper carrier bag containing the biscuits and my nasty blue gymslip onto the floor.

"Look at mi new dress, Nanna." I twirled around in front of her to show it off. "Int it lov'ly?" Nanna agreed and wiped her eyes on the frayed cuff of her cardigan. "An' look at mi new ball." I bent down and extracted it from another brown paper carrier bag, chucked it into the air and bounced it on the stone flags.

After recovering from the shock, Nanna settled herself down to listen to the tale of how I'd been stolen. Kitty was wild and told it with relish.

All I could do was dash through to the kitchen. Everything was just as I had left it… well almost. It was still a muck 'ole. A fly crawled over the lip of Graham's cracked pint pot[*]. More flies weaved round the window till I went too near, and they broke ranks with angry zuzzes. Somebody had been scattering

---

[*] *With a man in a smock and 'Tykes motto' on.* "See all, hear all, say nowt. Eat all, sup all, pay nowt. And if tha does owt for nowt, allus do it for thinsen.

143

currants around. The floor near the window was sprinkled with them, there were some near the other cups, and on the table. Was Arnold back? But when I looked properly, they were dead flies. I pushed aside the tattered black curtain, which was still the stairs door, and whizzed upstairs and down again.

What did it matter that everything stank of damp, and was wrapped in dust and soot. So what if the slop bucket was half full. This was home.

"Go n' put kettle on 'eather," said Kitty, "an' scald us all a pot er tea."

I flew back into the kitchen and shooed away a bulbous bluebottle crawling all over the sugar bag. By the time I'd taken in the pots, in various patterns of chips, cracks and discolour, Kitty had got out the mixed biscuits.

"'ere, get some er these h'eaten." She pushed the bag in front of our noses. Nanna nibbled on one in silence. I dunked mine in my tea, tracing one of the cracks like a river down the pot to its source at the base of the handle stump. Kitty was slurping, and munching toothless between exciting tellings of the tale.

Suddenly she caught sight of Nanna's little pocket watch[**], hanging from its chrome stand on the bedside table. "Bloody 'ell. Is it that time already? She lifted it up for a closer look. "It's time ah were off. H'If ah'm quick ah'll just catch t'downill bus. It's due in two minutes."

With that she picked up her purse and hopped it. I didn't mind. I was alone again, at home with Nanna.

Ah'm gunner play out wi mi new ball now, Nanna." I grinned throwing it in the air like an expert juggler.

"Well, mind that road. Remember it's busy – ah don't want yer getting' knocked down now yer've just cum back 'ome."

I stood on the step savouring the space, the freedom, the sunshine. Then bouncing my ball on the uneven flagstones I thought about what I could do next. Holding the ball safely, I ran down the steps, along the passage, past the 'owd 'ouse and into the lane like a little bird that had just been released from its cage.

Still in a dreamlike state I trotted down Private Road past the crooked stone fence posts and the iron gate. Beads of brilliance glimmered through branches and lit my way through the green of leaves and meadows, and glinting chinks in windows on the hill to my right. Before me loomed the great grey shape of March Hill, like the head and tail of a friendly whale, sinking back into the moor after welcoming me home, the further down the lane I ran. Round the bend, and little sparrows flitted from branch to branch. In the meadow sheep looked up from their grazing. My energy, locked up for so many months, suddenly burst out with the sun once I'd run past all the trees to the waterfall.

[**] *Now on Graham's mantelpiece.*

Eastergate, when I got there, was as good as a page from Rupert. Over the narrow cobbled bridge to hot grass, cool water and sky bluer than a bluetits cap. The brightest things around were amethyst spires of Foxgloves, which waved to me, whispering, "Welcome back, Heather." I waved back, and ran on.

It was a pity Arnold couldn't share all this with me.

I walked back in my own time, dodging nettles and smelling smells. When I got home I was met by quiet, and Nanna's smile. After making Nanna and me a pot of tea, I spotted a Rupert annual in the cupboard and I sank into the battered old couch with it.

At six o'clock Graham arrived home from the mill.

"Well, ah'll be buggered," he exploded as he came through the door. "Wen did you cum wom?"

I smiled, "Mi mammy fetched me today." (as if I was the pound of mixed biscuits she'd bought earlier).

Graham looked at Nanna "Did tair[*] know she were cumin' wom?"

"No. Yer mother never came up n' said owt t'me. She just turned up wi' 'er on t' doorstep. But ah'm glad she did... Heather's had a terrible time in that 'ome. Tell 'im about it Heather."

Graham rubbed his eyes and stared hard at me again. "Well, ah can't get over

---

[*] *You.*

it. I thought tha were there fer good." He smoothed back his hair and flopped down on the sofa to recover from the shock. "Where's yer mother nair[**] then?"

"She'll 'ave gone back t'yond Topczewski." Nanna scowled.

"Wat 'appened then, ow did it cum about 'at she brought yer wom?"

"Ah wer on mi way t'school wi' two er t'other girls. An' next thing ah knew she jumped out from behind a high wall."

Graham tittered. "Do 'they' know yer wom then?"

I mentioned Miss Newton.

"Well ah nivver," tittered Graham again, raising himself off the sofa. He went into the kitchen whistling.

As in every ointment though – there's always a fly. At about seven o'clock, after Graham had gone to do some nakklin in the owd 'ouse, I was sitting on the couch reading one of my old Bunty comics. Suddenly, there was the shuddering hum of a car slowing down, and tyre noise outside the window. I looked up from my Bunty. The engine stopped, so did my heart – almost. I ran to the window. An official looking bespectecled woman slipped out of a black car. She was carrying a brief case… and she was coming towards *our* door.

"Sumdi's 'ere, Nanna," I squeaked, not knowing whether to run for Graham or not.

"Who is it?"

The door was ajar so she simply knocked and flounced in. "Hello. My name's Christine Jones and I'm from the Welfare Office in Huddersfield. As you may have guessed I'm here to talk to you about Heather. Is Mrs Top…chew…ski here?" She stumbled.

I wasn't prepared to say Mrs Top…che…ski had hopped it, and just looked at her blankly.

"Well, anyway, what your daughter did this morning was wrong – very wrong. She had no right to just take Heather without informing us."

Christine Jones' eyes widened like two huge flowery rosettes, her frock was all pink flowers, she smelt of flowers, but sounded like Miss Newton.

"Heather's had a bad time in that there 'ome and ah'm glad Kitty did wat she did." Nanna defended. "Ah didn't know whether ah were ever gunner see 'er again."

"That's beside the point," Christine Jones frowned and shook her head, her poodle perm shook with her. "There are procedures to follow and I'm sure your daughter is well aware of this. If she had come to us in a 'proper manner' I'm sure we could have sorted something out. A word with matron maybe or a visit home." What ever was Christine Jones on about? No one at the Cottage Homes had been prepared to listen to any questions of mine. "As it was, we had no idea

[**]*Now.*

where Heather was... she could have been anywhere. I'm sure you'll agree your daughter acted very irresponsibly. Anyway," her cheeks were really blooming now, "I will need to see where Heather sleeps."

What on earth had 'SLEEP' got to do with owt after everything I'd been through? It was up to me to come up with an answer, fast.

"Mi bed's upstairs," I lied. Graham was busy in the owd 'ouse, and Nanna said nothing.

"Would you mind showing me then?" Christine Jones was like a weed you couldn't get shut of. I led her through our damp, dingy kitchen, the tattered black curtain and up the uncarpeted steps into Graham's room.

She rooted herself in the doorway, slowly taking it all in; glancing from the Brylcreem on the marble washstand to the big black comb spiderlegged with bits of Graham's hair. Her eyelids folded like falling petals when she saw the pair of imitation gold cufflinks and Graham's best shoes placed neatly beside Graham's bed. But she didn't comment. I suddenly saw myself in her car, shooting off to Dewsbury – and I didn't like it. I couldn't allow her down the stairs until she had promised me faithfully that she was not going to take me back. If she pondered and puzzled I could be out of the door and down Private Road in seconds. Arnold had done it with the School Board Man and so could I.

I put myself between her and the stairs, and just blurted it out. "I am NOT going back to live in THAT HOME n' nubdi can make me! Ah'll run away first. I 'ated it there... they were 'orrible t'me." Then in a tiny voice that was more of a plea than a demand, added, "Please don't make me go back there, ah want t' stop 'ere wi' mi Nanna. Mi brother's grown up an' can look after me."

Christine Jones looked down at me and although it was dark on the stairs I could see sympathy somewhere in the two black seed pods of her eyes.

"It's alright, Heather. I'm not going to take you back to the Cottage Homes. I can see that you prefer it here with your grandma. But - you must promise me that you will attend school regularly. It's very important. You can't just run around all day doing as you please. "

Roses suddenly bloomed at Millstone Cottage. And so did Christine Jones, smiling down at me with teeth flashing white in the poor light. I smiled back. "Ah promise that ah'll never... not ever... have a day off again. Ah'll go on Mundi... honest."

"Good. Now are you going to let me past or am I going to stay here all night?"

That night I slept soundly in Nanna's bed. No more getting up in a morning to bacon, eggs, horrible kids and 'neat hospital folds'.

PART 6

CHAPTER TWENTY-TWO

AUTUMN '60

If Christine Jones had been hanging about outside the County School before nine on Monday, she would not have been disappointed. I simply 'turned up' in the playground and carried on as if I had never been away. And still fairly clean too! Pat and Margaret were delighted to see me and came rushing over like two excited puppies.

"Where 'ave yer been?" asked Pat, fussing over me. "Mi mum said yer were in an orphanage er summet." She put her arms around me and we began walking towards the monkey bars. I didn't want to talk about it and brushed it aside with a "Yer ah wor - but ah'm back 'ome now."

"Let's go n' play on t'swings," said Margaret, tugging at my hand. I cheered as Margaret began dragging me across the playground. Lynn Wilkinson, who had just come through the top gate and looked like a beautiful pink bird I'd seen in a book once, in her fluffy bolero, shouted, "Can I play?" She didn't seem to notice that I was there or that I had been missing for so long. For the next ten minutes we took it in turns to share at two swings and dare each other to do the 'bumps'.[*] My real friends were so different to the ones in the Cottage Homes.

For once I didn't feel out of place. I was still wearing the new dress from Woolworths, bought for me by the woman that I used to call Mammy and would again. I hadn't had it off my back since the day I'd walked out of the public lavatories. It was a bit creased through sleeping in it, and it had become a bit grubby down the front where I'd been carrying sticks - but overall it didn't look too bad. At least I looked summery - like the rest of my friends.

At nine o'clock the bell went and between them Pat and Margaret led me through the entrance, across the big hall and into a large square room that overlooked the park.

"Sit 'ere," said Margaret, pointing to one of the little wooden desks that had an inkwell in one corner.

My new teacher turned out to be Mr Armitage who I remembered from before. He was bald and round and small. After introducing himself and asking

---

[*] *Going high enough for the chains to go slack for a second, before 'bumping' tight again.*

what my name was, he said it was nice to see me and hoped I would settle in well.   He also told me that he would sort me out with a pen and paper after assembly. I smiled then, and Dewsbury felt far away.

June Crabtree, Lesley Davis and Pauline Hill still sat where they always sat, and as usual Martin Brown was at the back of the classroom. He'd always found lessons difficult. After register, Mr Armitage took out the dark blue ledger from the cupboard I'd last seen almost a year ago, and began collecting the dinner money. Thankfully, Graham had left me two half crowns on top of the sideboard the night before. He'd said, "We don't want yer lookin' daft on yer first day back, do we?" We all went into assembly and I sang 'Glorious things of thee are spoken, Zion, city of our God' louder than I'd sung it before.

Back in class, Mr Armitage came up to me and said that if I didn't have any dinner money *next* week it didn't matter, Mr Carr was going to 'sort things out' for me.

"Who's going to tell Heather what we always start lessons with?"   Mr Armitage asked the class.

Everyone immediately blew out their chests, stuck their hands in the air as high as they could and shouted, "Me! Me!"

"Very well then, seeing as you're all so enthusiastic, we'll all say it together. Now remember Heather probably hasn't heard this before so speak loudly and clearly. Right then let's begin."

"Good... better... best. Never... let... it... rest," everyone chanted. "Till... your... good... is... better... and... your... better... best."

"Now did you hear that, Heather?"

"Yes sir." I smiled.

He passed me an exercise book from a tall cupboard at the front of the classroom. He also gave me a long-handled, thin-nibbed pen and topped up my inkwell with Stevenson's Ink. The exercise book was so neat and new, and much like a bed with crisp, clean sheets, that I made my mind to do only my 'best' handwriting in it.

Mr Armitage copied the poem onto the blackboard, repeating it as he chalked.

"Remember that Heather," he said, "and you'll never go far wrong..."

At playtime I spent some of my bus fare on a packet of Potato Puffs from the tuck shop, as a reward to myself for returning to my own school.

And Mr Carr did indeed 'sort things out', he made it all right for me to have free school meals.

Unlike the times I had trailed back hopeless from Dewsbury Moor School, I skipped across the road from the County School that day. On the way home I ran into Frank Mayle's Sweet Shop and bought two penny bubbly gums and a flying saucer. Frank was surprised to see me.

"Well, well, you've grown a bit since I last saw you," he smiled as he put the sweets into a little conical bag. Then I met up with Patricia who had just been to Dixon's to buy a packet of fags for her gran. I had already eaten the yellow sherbet disc but I gave her one of my bright pink bubbly gums.

"Bet I can blow a bigger bubble than you," I grinned.

"Bet yer can't," she said, and together we stood on the pavement chewing like sheep, each trying to out-blow the other.

We looked in the shop windows. "Bagsy them Dari-Rich chocolates," cried Pat.

"Bagsy that box of White Heather Assortment," I grinned.

We 'bagsied' this and 'bagsied' that, until there was absolutely nothing else left to 'bagsy'. Then Patricia said she had better take the cigs back to her gran. "Yer can cum wi me if yer want," she smiled. Her gran only lived across the road from Pat, at number four. She invited me in, to watch television.

My own Nanna welcomed me back the moment I got home and asked me piles of questions about what I'd been up to all day. Listening to me chuntering on about all my friends, Good-better-best, and the custard creams I'd eaten at Pat's Grans, might have been for her a bit like listening to a monologue on the Light Programme.

One thing which had changed for the worst since I'd settled back at home was the Reed's next door had moved up Woods Avenue, and had been replaced by Navvy Jones (no relation to Christine) who was definitely not the same. But despite Navvy Jones and his nakklin' noise (he used to chop chicken up on the wall. Moss, grit and muck all went in the pan with it) it was nice to curl up on the tickin next to Nanna, relating stories of flights on my moorland aeroplane. I'd been to America, Canada and the places I'd seen in my Rupert books. If I hadn't been flying I'd been paddling in the stream up Eastergate. Sometimes I would read Nanna snippets of stories out of my Bunty, and she'd remark on what a 'good scholar' I was.

One night, after bronze and gold had replaced the hundred shades of green down Private Road, when there was no coal and the last of our candle had burnt out hours ago, we decided to entertain ourselves by watching the lights from passing cars flicker across the wall then disappear in a yellow semi-circle of light. Without warning, there was a loud rapping at the door. Mammy? Topczewski? Please not Miss Newton and Mr Bruce! My throat dried up and the car lights became one big flicker round my head.

"Who is it?" called Nanna.

"Reynold... Reynold Quarmby," stuttered the disembodied voice from behind the door.

"Go n' let 'im in," whispered Nanna. "It's only Reynold, e'll be lookin' fer our Graham."

Relieved, I jumped out of bed and ran across the freezing floor to the door. Reynold was a tall, young man of about twenty-one. I'd seen him a couple times since Kathleen's funeral and thought he was nice. Once, he had even bought Arnold and me a tin of toffees for Christmas. Even knowing this, it took my chest long enough to stop pounding.

"Ah've just popped up t'see if Graham's about," he said, stepping into the dark room.

"He's not in," said Nanna. "Ah think 'e said 'e were goin' t'see Barry Christopher n' Malcolm."

I shot back to bed.

"Close t'door behind yer," said Nanna. "It's a bit cowd in 'ere." From under the greasy blanket I could hear the rub of the trestle as it brushed across the stone flags. Then the little click of the Yale latch as it caught the sneck. For a moment he stood not quite knowing what to do in the coalless, electricless dark.

"Mmm... ah've brought mi... er... pianer accordion wi' me." He murmured as I snuggled down at the side of Nanna. "Erm... would yer like me t'play yer a few tunes? Ah can play almost owt."

Nanna thought for a minute. "Can yer play Que Sera Sera?"

Reynold didn't answer. Instead he began fumbling about with the little silver clips on his leather carrying case. Peeping over Nanna's shoulder I could just make out the peculiar little piano and his dangly arms as they slipped through the narrow strip of his shoulder strap. Every now and then there was a flash of ivory, then he squeezed the bellows in and out with one hand, tapped the keys with the other and began 'tuning up'. Before long the sound of music filled the room.

> Que Sera Sera
> What ever will be will be
> The future's not ours to see
> Que Sera Sera.

I knew most of the words from listening to it on the Housewife's Choice. I also knew that Nanna liked this song because it helped her to make sense of why Kathleen had died. When the song finished, so did Nanna's humming, with a contented smile.

He played 'The Yellow Rose of Texas', 'Catch a Falling Star' and 'The

Happy Wanderer'. As I val de re, val da ra-ed ...with him, I was hiking across the moors on a warm sunny day.

"Bet yer don't know this one?" said the grey shape of Reynold.

Nanna said she did and began humming the tune softly.

"What about this one then?" 'Just a song at twilight when the lights are low and the flickering shadows seem to come and go.'

Reynold seemed to be enjoying entertaining us just as much as we were enjoying his unexpected concert, despite the show being carried out in the shadows of car headlamps. Reynold said it was a good job he could play from memory, which was just as well as the only bit of light he had was from the gas lamp down the road shining through the window.

After about half an hour of fun, Reynold asked Nanna if she had one last request. She had. 'The Old Rustic Bridge By The Mill'. It was a very old song and not one that Reynold was quite as familiar with - but he did his best and Nanna enjoyed it...

"Nice lad, that," sighed Nanna, after Reynold had wished us a pleasant evening and wood was back in t'oyle.[*]

By the time Private Road was crispy toast to walk on, and matron at The Homes would have been disgusted to see my appearance now, I had let on a new project - to save up for a donkey. (I already had five shillings put away at the back of the cupboard and hoped by the end of the year to have at least ten bob.) I planned on keeping my little donkey in a lush green field down Private Road End. The paddock belonged to Little Tommy. I hadn't asked him if I could use it yet but I was certain he'd let me.

"Ah'm gunner get a donkey instead of a norse," I told Nanna, "cos donkeys look cheaper." Nanna just listened with a smile.

I had also been busy filling in my 'Horse and Pony' scrapbook. Reluctant to cut up my comics, I did sometimes snip the odd picture out. But, there was another source of material, newspaper cuttings. One picture in particular had grabbed my attention - Princess Anne holding the reins of a fuzzy-maned pony. The Princess was all dressed up in posh riding clothes: fawn jodhpurs, tweed jacket, black velvet riding hat. One day, I wanted to look like that.

When I wasn't snipping, scratting up lucky stones or attending school, (I hadn't actually had a day off since my promise to Christine Jones) I was wandering around the moors, on brown days, on grey days, or short cool blue days.

I had plenty to do, Nanna, Graham, friends, but no Arnold, and stranger

---

[*] *Door was shut.*

still (or maybe not), no Mammy. She'd left Towngate and folk said she'd flitted to Milnsbridge. So she really had hopped it.

CHAPTER TWENTY-THREE

NOV '60

After about six months of being back home, Nanna seemed to deteriorate. Her hair was matted and stuck to her head like a dirty dishcloth. The more I went on about my exploits, the less she seemed to take in. But I told her anyway.

"Navvy Jones has fallen over his electric heater again Nanna, and all t'wires on t'leads 'as come out. He's asked Graham if he's got a minute to shove em all back." Nanna did no more than glance up. "Ah bounced mi ball all the way to school today, Nanna, and after school ah went t'Pat's gran's again t'watch Johnny Morris." But nothing.

Rain came, and soddened the leaf path. Wind came and spiralled the sodden leaves in my face when I was stickin'. Candles burned down, and at one point another cup lost a handle. Graham said "Never 'eed, that's lahf." Nanna didn't notice.

There was a ghostliness about her face and she could barely eat anything. Her arms were sticks and her fingers splinters. She was like a wooden doll. I'd often heard of people 'wasting away' and I wondered if that was what Nanna was doing.

One Sunday morning Graham said that I must go to Milnsbridge, (six miles away on the bus) find Mammy and tell her that Nanna was 'badly'. "Conductor'll tell yer where Whitely Street is," he said.

"Whitely Street, love?" The conductor smiled as he clipped my ticket. "It's across from t'Warren 'ouse pub. Ah'll tell yer when we get there."

The bus was almost empty, so too was the road. The middle of Marsden looked like Nanna, pale and vacant. I wished Mrs Reed still lived next door, she could've come with me. Instead, I'd bumped into Navvy Jones who'd hiccupped "Ah've dropped some pound notes, have yer seen 'em?" He'd done that trick before, and somehow found them, washed them in a bowl of water, dried them in front of the fire and nearly burnt them.

And so I had to go on the bus alone and find Mammy myself.

As we got going, I recognised some of the scenery from the time Mammy had 'pinched' me from the Cottage Homes: smears of Christmas puddingy hens scratting, Sparth Reservoir rippling with silver black. Then came Slaithwaite, (where I'd nearly fainted while waiting for th'up bus after seeing Jill for the last time), Linthwaite and rows of sunless houses.

"This is your stop, love," called the conductor as the bus drew to a halt opposite the Warren House. "That's the road, down there." He pointed to a steep hill running down from Manchester Road.

All feelings of safety and security disappeared with the ting of the bell and the roar of the engine, as the bus set off towards Huddersfield. I stood alone on the pavement. Then I remembered Graham had told me Mammy lived at number fifteen, which, 'fer owt 'e knew', was a little back to back. I slowly set off to find her.

Whitely Street was anything but. Not even the yellowest of sunshine would have unclogged the grime from windows and doorsteps, or dazzled colourless curtains. In weed-choked gardens, rickety gates hung off rusty hinges. Cigarette ends, lollipop sticks and sweet wrappers cowered behind walls.

A little way along the road I turned into what I thought might lead onto the back to backs - a sort of grassy ginnel with a row of run-down cellar dwellings built on top of a steep bank. As I made my way along the narrow path I could see the slanting roofs of a big mill in the valley bottom. The rooftops were so close I felt that if I held out my hand I could touch them.

Number fifteen, with its black paint-peeled door, was the third one on. I knocked, expecting Mammy to come rushing out all of a flap, then expecting Mammy to be out, and Topczewski to answer instead, and peer wordlessly at me. Then not knowing who or what to expect at all, I bit my lip. There was no reply. I knocked again. Standing back, I looked up at the windows but there was no sign of life. I stood stupidly on the cracked step, wondering what to do. Graham had stressed that I *must* find Mammy. Just then, I heard a scraping sound coming from next door, a moment later the door opened.

"Who yer lookin' fer, love?" asked a large lady in a dirty pinny and faded pink carpet slippers.

"Mi Mammy."

"An' who's yer Mammy?"

"Mrs. Topczewski."

"Oh, 'er. Well, she's flitted."

"Flitted?"

"Aye. She moved a few months ago... but ah can tell yer where she's gone. See that row er 'ouses over there?" She pointed somewhere to the right of us. "That's where she lives now... or at least she did last time ah saw͵'er."

I made as if to walk in that direction but she stopped me. "Yer can't get that way, love... there's a brick wall there. Yer'll 'ave t' go back on to t'main road, down some steps n' through a tunnel. Yer can't miss it though... it's first lot er steps yer cum to. Ah think she lives at number ten."

With relief I thanked her and ran off. It wasn't far to the flight of steps, and the lady was right, you couldn't miss them. They were steep and dusty, and I hurried through the passage without looking back, to find myself in a similar place to where I had just been - another row of little back to backs overlooking the big mill.

There looked to be about six houses in all, each with a little flagged path leading to a door. Number Ten was the third one on. Again I knocked. Again I bit my lip. And again I waited, wondered, knocked harder. This time I could hear footsteps and the latch being lifted. I moved away, just in case it was 'That bloody foreigner'. If it is Topczewski, I thought, ah'm not goin' in.

It was Mammy.

"Wat *you* doin' 'ere?" she shrieked.

"Graham seys mi Nanna's 'badly' n' yer've t'cum back wi' me."

"Badly! 'ow badly!" She shifted from one foot to the other.

"Ah don't know… she won't eat owt…n' she's gone thin."

"Cum in a minute." She led me into a tiny room. The first things I saw were half a dozen or so empty VP wine bottles strewn across a blue Formica table. So she was still living with him. She would never drink that much wine herself… surely.

"Sit down a minute while ah get mi coat," Mammy said. She disappeared into another room and I perched on the edge of the nearest chair, a dark maroon rocker with upholstered arms and a fringed cushion. There were empty green bottles, the smell of cheap wine, but no sign of Topczewski himself, so I sat back further into the chair to study the room. It was pretty much like the one she had rented in Marsden, neat and tidy. A small fire burnt in the hearth and a few jumble sale ornaments stood stiffly on the tiled mantleshelf above it. In the window bottom a large alsation stared across at me. It had huge pointy ears and wide eyes. Its plaster tongue dripped out of the corner of its plaster mouth, its two front paws were crossed, dog-like. Despite the fact it was covered in chips and scratches, it looked real.

A 'Whistling Boy', stood on top of the sideboard, prim in wide brimmed plaster hat and kneelength plaster britches. He didn't look at all bothered that he was living with the Goblin.

"*He's* in there, sleepin it off," tweeted Mammy. She had returned with a shabby mac in one hand and an old brown bag in the other. She waved in the direction of the door through which she had just come. Her beady eyes flashed. "He's been suppin' all bloody morning. 'e'll be as sour as vigginer[**] wen 'e wakens up an' wonders where I am, but let 'im wonder. Cum on let's get up t'that bus stop n' see wat's up wi' mi mother."

Back at the cottage Nanna didn't seem to know that we were there. Her cheeks were pale and sunken and her eyes were shut tight.

"Mother," warbled Mammy. "Wat's up wi yer. Our Graham seys yer not s'

[**] *Mammy's word for vinegar.*

well."   She nudged the old lady gently on the shoulder, but there was no response.

"She's still breathing but it sounds er bit funny," Mammy continued. "An' she dunt look s' good. She's a funny colour. Ah think we ought t'send fer t'doctor.

Ah think she's gone war[*] in't last 'our," said Graham.

"She's been like this before though, an't she?" I whispered, looking for reassurance. "Don't yer remember wen she nearly got pneumonia?"

Graham shook his head and said, "Well, ah don't reightly know. Ah don't reightly know."

He went into the kitchen for his shabby overcoat and extracted a few coppers from the sideboard drawer, "fer t'telephone. Ah'll ring from t'café," he said as he left.

He hadn't been gone long when there was a knock on the door. "Bloody 'ell 'es been quick," said mammy, expecting it to be the doctor. But it was only Mrs Reed. She had no idea Nanna was ill, and had just popped in to see how we all were. It was almost as if the spark man had been on that bus with me this morning.

The doctor didn't arrive until later. He knocked briskly on the door and walked straight in. With him came a rush of cold air which made the candle flicker. It would almost have gone out if Graham hadn't managed to revive it by giving it a swift blow, then with his hand around the candle to guard the flame; he walked over to the recess and placed it on the table beside Nanna's bed.

"H'it's mi mother," said Mammy. "She's..." Her voice fell into one of those whispers I wasn't supposed to hear.

I couldn't really hear what she was saying but from where I was sitting I could see that the doctor was giving Nanna a thorough examination. Then he had a quiet word with Mammy and the two of them went outside. Graham and Mrs Reed squinted at each other across the dimly lit room. The doctor must be telling Mammy what to get from the chemist. I'd have bet my Bunty it was Carter's Little Liver Pills. When they returned, the Doctor picked up his bag and bid us Goodnight. Mammy didn't say anything. Instead she came over to the fire and gave it a good poke.

A little later, after a pot of tea and some Arrowroot biscuits, Mrs Reed asked me if I would like to stay at her house for the night. "You can go straight to school from there in the morning," she suggested. "It's not far - just down the road - you'll be there in quick-sticks." She even promised me Ovaltine for

---

[*] *Worse.*

supper. I was a bit reluctant to leave Nanna, but Graham promised him and Mammy would look after her.

As we stood at the bus stop, the shadowy figures of Mammy and Graham hovered about in the candlelight. Every other house round about was bright with electricity.

After getting off the bus at the top of Brougham Road, Mrs Reed and I walked side by side up Rose Hill and into Woods Avenue council estate. I'd never been before but through the orange glow of the street lamps I could see it was similar to Dirker. Each house had its own garden, a tiny brick coalhole and a narrow path leading both to the front and back door. Mrs Reed led the way to the back door.

"I bet Bill's watching t'goggle box," she remarked as she opened the door and flicked a switch. The whole room burst into light. From the other room came the sound of muffled laughter.

"Tek yer coat off, love," smiled Mrs Reed, "and pop it on that chair."

Mr Reed was, as his wife had predicted, sitting on a comfy couch glued to a brown Bakelite television set.

"Hello, Heather." He looked up at me with a big grin. "What are you doing here?"

"She's stopping the night, Bill. Aren't you, Heather."

"Yes, n' ah'm goin' straight t'school from 'ere in't mornin'."

Mr Reed looked surprised but gave me a welcoming smile.

"You'd better come and sit down then." He pointed to the couch beside him.

The house seemed so light and cosy after Nanna's – no dark scratched furniture, just cheerful carpets, warm lamps, pretty pictures and a shiny sideboard. There were red curtains with black and yellow splashes on them and above our heads a large white lampshade like a flying saucer. Sitting on the mantleshelf was a slender glass cat with sticky-out blob eyes and bubbles of colour on its hindquarters.

Mrs Reed had disappeared into the kitchen to make a pot of tea.

"Tell Heather what yer watchin'," she shouted through the door.

It was 'What's My Line'.

"Have yer seen this before?" asked Mr Reed. "That's Isobel Barnett, sat at that there desk."

I hadn't seen it but it certainly looked funny. An old man of about forty appeared to be doing some sort of a silly mime.

Mrs Reed returned moments later with a tray of steaming hot tea and a plate full of biscuits. As I sat on the settee sipping the tea and enjoying the warmth of the fire I thought how nice it would be for me and Nanna to live with people like Mr and Mrs Reed.

"You can sleep in a pair of my old pyjamas," Mrs Reed said, later, in the bathroom, throwing me a pair of pink flowered ones through the door.

"And there's a towel over there." She pointed to the bath where a blue one with orange stripes hung over the rim. "And I've put you some toothpaste and a brush on top of the sink." She smiled, then closed the door and left me to it.

After playing with the taps for a few minutes, I thought I'd better be getting on with it, and filled the sink with the hot water. I quickly swilled my hands and most of my face with fancy pink soap. It was much better than those six sterile sinks from a few months ago. Afterwards, I brushed my teeth sideways, removed my dirty clothes and put on the pair of clean pyjamas left out for me. Mrs Reed laughed when she saw me in them. "Come 'ere n' let me turn them up at the sleeves and the feet for you."

I followed her into her bedroom. Whilst she fiddled about rolling up the pyjamas, I looked around the room. Against the wall opposite the window, were what looked like treasures from someplace Rupert might have flown to on a magic carpet; minorets of scent, turrets of nail varnish and towers of talcum powder rose up from their rich walnut dressing table. Mrs Reed saw me admiring them and asked me if I would like to smell at them.

"This is my favourite," she grinned, passing me a vial of 'Black Rose'. "Here smell at it. It's lov'ly." She unscrewed the top and pushed it under my nose. "Bill bought it me for Christmas last year. It's made by Goya."

It smelt of Eastern Promise. Mrs Reed dabbed a little onto my neck and wrist.

"And that's mi Crème puff." She pointed to a round plastic case of peachy makeup.

Then we moved onto the nail varnish: Calypso Pink, Pink Blush and Flame.

"Here, let's put you some hand lotion on an'all." She took a blob of 'Nivea, Blue Velvet' and rubbed it onto the palm of my hand.

Back downstairs, Mr Reed had mended the fire and was sitting with his feet propped on a brown leather pouffe. He was puffing away at a cigarette.

"You can stop up a bit and watch telly with us if you want." Mrs Reed said. "Sit down here and I'll go and get you some supper. She flew off into the kitchen and returned moments later with the promised pot of Ovaltine and a Cadbury's chocolate biscuit. Mr Reed kept cracking jokes and Mrs Reed kept fetching him a swipe with the cushion. "You do say the daftest things," she teased. But I thought he was right funny.

When it came time for me to go to bed Mrs Reed took me up to the spare room. It was just like Rupert's, Rupert's small wardrobe, Rupert's little bed, with Rupert's pink padded quilt all comfy on top. Mrs Reed showed me how to switch the lamp off, "I'm only downstairs, if you need me - just give me a shout."

As she descended the stairs I could hear the fall of her foot on each step. The moment she had gone I began to feel funny – sort of sad. I even began to wish I was back home. I just needed to know Nanna was okay.

"What would you like for breakfast, Heather?" Asked Mrs Reed the next morning as she slid open the glass doors of a kitchen cabinet. "There's cornflakes, Weetabix, toast, scrambled eggs, porridge." The list seemed endless. In the end I chose cornflakes which arrived in a blue melamine bowl with lots of milk and sugar on. Seated at the 'wipe clean' table, I crunched my way through the cereal, while Mrs Reed lit up a fag. Plumes of grey smoke rose from her hand like fumes from a tailpipe. In between mouthfuls of hot tea poured from a blue flowery teapot, she wheezed and choked like an old tractor.

There were no piles of rags in this kitchen, unlike ours, but loads of modern stuff, something for doing toast in, something for scrubbing linoleum with, an electric kettle, a Hoovermatic washing machine, and the trusty Bush wireless that I had seen many times at No 2.

Mr Reed had already set off for work but Mrs Reed said he had left me sixpence to spend at the tuck shop. "He says you've to buy yourself some sweets or summet." I did a quick calculation and reckoned I had enough to buy two Jammy Dodgers and a packet of Potato Puffs.

"Cum on, love," said Mrs Reed "We don't want yer late fer school." After helping me on with my coat, she said, "It's been lov'ly 'avin' you, you must come again sometime."

She walked me to the gate and stood waving until privet blocked her from sight.

CHAPTER TWENTY-FOUR

NOV '60

That afternoon when I came out of school Mrs Reed was waiting for me by the gates. "I thought I'd walk yer t'bus stop," she said. "'Av'e just been t'Co-op t'buy some bread – n' ah saw 'at school were lozin*. 'Ave yer 'ad a good day?"

I had, and was looking forward to telling Nanna about Mrs Reed's house, the television, hand cream, an'all. But Mrs Reed looked a bit vacant and started stamping her feet as though she were cold.

"What have you been doing at school then today?" She asked.

"Nowt much, apart from some sums n' sewin'".

"When I was at school," she said, "I used to like geography best." She slipped a packet of Wills Woodbine from her coat pocket and a lit up a cigarette. She took a slow pull and exhaled the smoke through her nostrils. "Ah used t'dream about all t'exotic places ah could visit when ah were grown up," she laughed. "But then ah met Bill n'... well, yer know 'ow it is?"

I nodded, not knowing 'ow it is'. When the bus came I clambered on, waving goodbye to Mrs Reed through the mucky glass. When I jumped off the bus at the top of Private Road, I could see that Mammy was standing on the doorstep and the curtains were pulled on. She was hopping about from one foot to the other. I had to squeeze past her to get in. I was no sooner through the door 'ole when my eyes were immediately drawn to the alcove. Instead of the old grey blanket, the mucky coat and Nanna, I saw a dazzling sheet covering the empty tickin'.

"Where's Nanna?" I gasped.

Mammy didn't answer.

"Where's mi Nanna?"

"She's dead," said Mammy.

The word echoed in my ears like some dreadful voice from beyond the grave, a nightmare voice like the one I'd heard in The Homes. I let out a piercing scream and ran to the door. "Nanna! Nanna!"

I didn't know where I was running to, but I had to get away from that horrible white sheet in the corner. Suddenly Graham appeared from somewhere and shot across the room and caught my arm. He held it tightly until I couldn't move. Unable to shake him off I stood there soaking his shirt with my tears, struggling for breath between sobs, aware all the while of the empty bed and this grotesque cover. For the first time in my life I had returned home and Nanna wasn't there.

---

* *Finishing.*

Everyone else had known the night before that Nanna was dying. That's what the doctor would have been telling Mammy, telling Graham, but not telling me.

"It 'ad t' 'appen one day, Heather," comforted Graham. "She was an old lady. None of us can live fer ever."

"But... ah... ah... wanted... 'er to," I sobbed. "Ah... wanted 'er to..."

"Cum n' sit on t'couch, it's been a shock fer yer, ah know it 'as." He led me across the dirty stone flags towards the sagging settee, and tried to comfort me as best he could.

"Mi mother'll mek yer a drink, won't yer Mother?" He waved her into the kitchen with a firm 'make yerself useful' gesture.

Mammy, hovering around in the background not knowing what to do, suddenly sprang into action and trotted off into the kitchen, returning moments later with a pot of warm, milky tea, which she pressed into my shaking hands.

"Ah weren't gunner tell yer she'd died," she moaned. "Ah... ah... were gunner tell yer she were in ospitle er summet so that yer didn't get upset. But that there bloomin' doctor Sumner said ah'd t' do no such thing. 'e said yer'd find out anyway so yer might as well know from t'start. Ah still think yer'd er been better off not knowin'."

The hospital idea did sound a bit bizarre, but I knew that it was only her bumbling way of trying to protect me. For a moment I almost wished that is what she had said. She was rocking backwards and forwards and as I looked up at her through bleary eyes I could see that her own eyes were moist with tears. She began rubbing her chin with her thumb and forefinger. I wanted to say, "Don't cry, Mammy," but instead bent my head over my pot, and sipped my tea.

As dusk gathered in the dingy room, Graham went to scrat about in the coal 'ole and before long a warm glow lit the room. The horrible white sheet was still there, crisp and sharp, like new paper. I didn't ask where it had come from but I imagined that Cousin Miriam had probably sent it. How come we needed a clean sheet now that Nanna had died.

"We won't put wireless on tonight," murmured Graham. "T'wunt seem right." He prodded the fire with the thin iron poker then threw on a few shovels of nutty slack.

Around six, Mrs Reed turned up, in case we needed owt, she said. Mammy's eyes were like mine, dry but red and puffy. Mammy put the kettle on the rib to boil and Graham disappeared into the 'owd ouse' to do some nakklin'. I sat on the couch pretending to read my Bunty, but I was really listening to Mammy and Mrs Reed talk quietly about Nanna.

"Ah knew she couldn't last much longer... She'd put a sixpence under her piller fer 'eather's bus fare this morning... Graham's teken Kathleen's coat from under er piller en put it in t'sideboard cupboard. We'll never get rid of it. No... we'll never get rid of it."

Mammy uncrossed her legs and turning away from Mrs Reed for a moment, reached across to stab the fire with the old poker. From over the top of my comic, I could see her fighting back tears. Mrs Reed lit up yet another cigarette. It was awful when she had to leave to catch the down-hill bus. "I have to get back to Bill," she said.

I didn't want to sleep in Nanna's bed now it was cold and empty. Graham suggested I sleep on the settee. Mammy curled up in the old easy chair next to me.

❧

"Mi Nanna died yesterdi," I told my friend Julie at playtime the next day. "She were eighty three."

Julie looked down from the rusty monkey bars. "Did yer cry?"

"Nah," I lied.

"Don't talk about it agen then," she said. So I didn't.

CHAPTER TWENTY-FIVE

Graham returned from the mill and made himself a pot of tea. Our curtains had stayed across all next day, and after school I returned home and cowered in its dark heart. He had tried to make things as comfortable as possible for us; adjusting the wick in the tilly lamp, replacing an old mantle with a new one and lighting the lamp with a thin wax taper he'd found on the mantlepiece. Mammy, who was staying at Nanna's to look after me, said he was probably going to see his lady friend, Muriel. I was wondering what Muriel looked like when there was a knock on the door.

"Who the 'ell's this?" Mammy jumped to her feet.

"If it's Navvy Jones askin' if ah've got a minute," called Graham from the kitchen where he was having a swill, "ah 'aven't."

But it wasn't our neighbour tripped over his fire again. Nor was it our old neighbour Mrs Reed, who I hoped would stop by again tonight. Through the mellow glow of the lamp in the door 'oyle I recognised the woman as Mrs Mcallister. I went to school with her boys Kevin and Stephen, and they all lived on Waters Road, next door but one to my friends Mr and Mrs Sheard. I'd been playing Cowboys and Indians with them one time and after galloping around, had become faint with hunger. I'd dared to ask if I could have a slice of dry bread, and one of them had sneaked in to get me just that. It was the most wonderful thing I had eaten for ages, square, white and soft enough to sleep in.

"Reason I'm here," Mrs Mcallister began, "is because James, that's my husband, and I, have talked it over and decided that now Mrs Peace has... er... passed away, we would like Heather to come and live with us."

I hadn't given much thought to who would look after me now Nanna had died, just assumed I'd look after myself as I did pretty much anyway. The words hit me like a whack off Jean Burrhouse.

"Course, she wouldn't be t'cock er t'middin' you understand. She'd have to tow the line like everyone else." Who did she think she was, with her neat bob of blonde hair, her smart wool coat and her smug 'cock'er t'middin'? White-haired witch! A sickly smile crossed her face and reminded me of Auntie Hell-sie. I cringed and planned my refusal speech.

"It's very kind of you to h'offer," said Mammy in a suitably grateful voice. "'eather won't be able t'stop 'ere wi' me, 'they' won't let 'er." ('they' - meaning that lot from the Welfare office) "Ah don't know wat h'ever's gunner 'appen to 'er, ah really don't." She began rubbing her chin with a bony forefinger and shaking her head in a worried way. Terror ate at me again. My insides shook more than Meryl's fists to think I might see her again. And what if Jean Livesey had returned?

"Well, she would have a good home with us," cackled the 'white-haired witch'. She drew me close and put an unwelcome arm across my thin shoulders. I had an almost irresistible urge to shove her away, but remembering how Nanna had always insisted on good manners I showed some restraint and smiled weakly. As she left I heard her whisper to Mammy, "we'll be in touch."

The door had hardly closed behind her when all my feelings gushed out over Mammy.

"I am NOT gunner go and live wi 'er 'n' 'er stupid family!" I screamed. "An' nobody can make me!" I began banging my fist on the sideboard and kicking the door. "Why did yer ever make 'er think that ah might?" Maybe if I told Mammy I'd bloody well knife her (the white-haired witch, not Mammy) she might just listen. But that wouldn't be me.

Mammy, not used to seeing me in such a temper, didn't know what to do. "Well, yer won't be h'able t' stop 'ere," she said. "Yer 'eard wat ah said, They won't let yer…"

"What's goin' on?" Graham came in, all ready for off.

"Nowt," said Mammy.

That night I hardly slept.

The following morning Mammy said that when the church clock struck three, I'd know Nanna was being buried and after lessons I must go to the Adult School for the funeral tea.

Although most of the time Nanna had been bed ridden, half-starved and half-asleep, just knowing she was there was enough to make me feel safe. She had set me standards of behaviour that I would make sure stayed with me for the rest of my life.

At three o'clock I looked - for what must have been the millionth time - at the big round clock at the front of the classroom. In the distance I heard the dismal bells of St Bartholomew's, and my throat swelled up.

In the classroom, pens and pencils were put away, tracing paper was folded neatly and finally we sang the evening prayer.

> *Now the day is over,*
> *Night is drawing nigh;*
> *Shadows of the evening*
> *Steal across the sky.*
>
> *Now the darkness gathers,*
> *Stars begin to peep,*
> *Birds and bees and flowers*
> *Soon will be asleep.*

Jesus, give the weary
Calm and sweet repose;
With thy tender blessing
May their eyelids close.

When the morning wakens,
Then may I arise
Pure, and fresh, and sinless
In Thy holy eyes...

If I should die before I wake
I pray the Lord
My soul to take.

Amen...

As all the other girls and boys made their way home, I walked solemnly to the Adult School, which years ago had been used only for adult education and now was a venue for functions like The Old Folks' Treat, wedding breakfasts and funeral teas.

According to Graham, Nanna's funeral arrangements had been dealt with, and paid for, by Nanna's other granddaughter, Miriam. It still seemed odd that Miriam's father, my Uncle Harold, (who had died a couple of years earlier), should leave instructions in his will for his mother to have a 'proper' funeral. Despite being a wealthy man he had hardly given her anything when she was alive. Perhaps it was his wife who had said; "If your mother's daft enough to look after Kitty's children...then let her... it has nowt to do with us!"

I'd asked Graham earlier that day "Why did Uncle Harold leave someone as nice as Nanna to clam t'death, 'specially when he was so rich and only lived down t'road. "It in't fair."

"Nay, lass," Graham shook his head.

Now, walking along, I wondered how my other brother was getting on. Had they told him, in that home he was in. Would he be inside the Adult School waiting for me?

As I slunk into the big hall, there was a wooden table, like a long coffin in the middle, laid out with a stiff white cover. It reminded me of that thing on Nanna's bed instead of Nanna. On the coffin-table, funereal plates held meek sandwiches of ham and meat paste. Seated at the table were a dozen or so people on tubular chairs. Some of them I recognised – some I didn't. Most were dressed in black or dark grey. And there was no Arnold.

Making my way across the floor to where Graham and Mammy were sitting, those people seemed like ghosts sipping tea from thick white cups and placing them onto thick white saucers. At either end of the table a couple of two-tier cake stands held a selection of stiff buns and formal biscuits.

"Get summet t'eat," said Mammy, passing me a plate from the table. Graham got up and walked over to a pile of chairs that were stacked by the far wall he returned with one for me. I somehow managed to eat an iced bun with a cherry on top. The tea was thick and white like the cup I drank it from.

"So this must be Heather?" said a lady's voice behind me. I turned round to look at the person who had spoken and found it to be a right fine lady of about forty-five, in a black two piece suit with a fur trim. Her auburn hair, which looked as if it had been washed and set that very morning, fell in soft waves around her chubby face.

"Yes this's H…eather," said Mammy.

"We've just been talking about you," said the 'fine lady', pushing her glasses further up her nose. "Edgar, this is Heather." She turned round to talk to a straight-haired little man who was sitting beside her. I assumed he was her husband. He too wore glasses - big thick brown ones.

"Hello," he smiled.

"Your mother tells me you don't want to live with, er…," the 'fine lady' stumbled over the 'White Haired Witch's' name

"Mrs. McH'allister," Mammy bleated

"So Edgar and I wondered if you would like to come and live with us? We have a little girl of about the same age as you - her name is Elizabeth."

So Mammy was still trying to get rid of me! So much for making it clear last night that I wasn't going to live with anybody! But I knew that I should smile politely at these two people - who I had never met before – but were kind enough to offer me a good home. I should really say, "Yes, thank-you. I would love to come and live with you… and Elizabeth." And be grateful that I wouldn't need to look after myself at Millstone Cottage. Instead I just smiled shyly. They must have took the smile to mean that I liked the idea, and Edgar went on to say how pleased Elizabeth would be to have me living with them. She had lots of nice toys and he was sure she would let me play with them. We could be like sisters.

Then they seemed to forget me for a bit and the conversation turned to Nanna. One of the ladies at the table turned out to be Nanna's sister, Hannah. (She was also the mother of the 'fine lady' who wanted me to go and live with them.) Hannah looked quite old – about ninety.

"She was always such a proud woman," she wept into her handkerchief. "Her little house at Fer 'ill* were spotless."

---

* *Fer Hill, Bolster Moor, near Slaithwaite.*

Apparently she had paid Nanna a visit when I was living in The Home and had been dismayed to find her living in such squalor. "Ah took 'er a bit er bakin' up," she said, "But ah was so upset when ah saw 'er... she'd no fire, and 'ardly any blankets on t'bed. Even t'electric were cut off. Poor Lily. She looked so miserable."

I couldn't think of her as being Nanna's sister. She seemed too old. Sisters were meant to be young like Kathleen and me.

At one point I saw Mammy and the well-to-do-woman talking in a corner. Every so often one or the other stole a glance at me. Later when most people had left, Graham thanked cousin Miriam for seeing to everything. Miriam smiled and said, "*It's* been a good do. I know my father would have been pleased. He always said he wanted *it* done properly. Look, why don't you take some of these sandwiches home with you? They'll only go to waste. I'll find a paper bag for you to put them in." She began scooping a few of the leftover bits of bread and ham onto an empty plate.

She disappeared through a door that slammed shut behind her. A minute or two later Mammy came across with our coats. Graham told her about the sandwiches and her currant eyes lit up.

When Miriam returned, she thrust the leftover sandwiches into a white paper bag (the sort we got Turog in when we bought it from the bakers.) She also put a handful of buns into another bag. Mammy loved fancy cakes – especially ones with icing on top.

"Here carry these, Heather," said Miriam, passing them to me.

After saying goodbye to Miriam and some of the ladies who had been helping with the tea, Graham, Mammy and I left the Adult School and headed for the bus stop. Graham said he wouldn't be coming home till later though... he was going to see Muriel. I sighed to myself. The house always seemed so miserable without him. He had a 'knack' for making it more homely.

On the way home, Mammy pointed to the graveyard. It was impossible to see through the dirty bus windows and dimly lit streets, but she said, "That's where yer Nanna's grave is... h'over there. She's buried on top er Kathleen... it's wat she always wanted." Her voice became somber, which made me feel somber too, and the journey back to Millstone Cottage seemed to take all night.

Mammy ground the key in the lock and pushed the door. The house was shrouded in darkness. Stumbling over to the sideboard, Mammy began fumbling for a candle, swearing loudly as she knocked the 'bloody thing' onto the floor. The old enamel candlestick rattled onto the stone flags.

"Where the 'ell's that gone?" grumbled Mammy as she scratted around blindly.

"It's 'ere," both candle and stick had landed near my feet.

"Pass the bloody thing 'ere then," she cried, as I bent down to feel for them.

Mammy found a box of matches from somewhere on the sideboard, and all I could hear were the familiar sounds of her being vexed as she struggled to take one out of the packet and strike it. Eventually a small flickering flame revealed a house that was filthy and in disarray. For some reason Mammy had pulled Nanna's old iron bedstead into the middle of the floor. The ghostly sheet had gone and the old ex-army coat and the rough blanket lay in a midden on top of the tickin'. The grate was empty. Lurking somewhere between the sideboard and the kitchen door was the slop bucket. I could smell it from where I was standing.

"Ah'll make us a pot er tea," twittered Mammy, and bumbled off into the dark kitchen to put the kettle on. She took the candle with her, leaving me standing alone amongst the dirty clutter of the cold living room. Eerie shadows lurched across the walls as the light from the candle flickered through the kitchen door.

We made a good supper out of what cousin Miriam had put in the bags and left some for Graham. Mammy suggested going to bed early as there was no coal left and it was too dark to go stickin'. As we lay side by side under the thin blanket the subject of me going to live with 'h'Alice and h'Edgar' came up.

"It's h'either them or t'Mc'h'allisters," she said matter of factly. "An' ah can tell yer don't want t'live wi' Mr 'n' Mrs Mc'h'allister." She shuffled her body further under the mucky blanket. "So there's nowt else for it, yer'll just ave t'go an' live wi h'Alice 'n' h'Edgar in Slaithwaite." She pulled the top of the blanket close around her and sleepily mumbled stuff about Nanna.

"Happen she'll come a-knockin'," she added.

I tried not to listen and screwed my eyes up tight.

CHAPTER TWENTY-SIX

The sky, that Sunday I was due to move out, was heavy and damp and clung to the surrounding hills like a thick grey blanket. After fetching a bucket of water and a few sticks I sat on the edge of the bed, chin resting on my knees. Not even the sight of my Rupert books piled high on the sideboard could cheer me up. Would Alice and Edgar be horrible and bossy just like all those other people in the Cottage Homes? And what about Elizabeth and all those nice toys? I'd have to settle down to a routine of rules and bathtimes and bedtimes. No wandering around the hillside from dawn till dusk scratting on Flint's Tip and forgetting the time. I could see the future now, stretching out before me like a long prison sentence.

Mammy was busy in the kitchen, fettlin' up. I could hear her shoving stuff about and the clanking of the dolly tub as she shifted it from one end of the kitchen to the other. Maybe she was thinking of leaving Topcezewski and staying here for good. Then why couldn't I stay with her? What had it got to do with people in welfare who I lived with? I only had to remember my time in the Cottage Homes to realise that I was far better off without them... and their 'It will be best for you' attitude. I knew what was best for me, and that was to stay at Millstone cottage and look after myself.

Graham got up shortly after ten. After having a quick swill in a basin of cold water he made himself a pot of tea then went out. He didn't say anything deep and meaningful about me leaving home, just "See yer later."

I kicked around the ragpile miserably, and suddenly spotted a hand. I pulled, and out came Violet who I hadn't seen since before the Homes. Brave Violet who was as shabby as me, her smile fraying. I wouldn't feel quite as scared at Alice and Edgar's if she was with me. But then I remembered Elizabeth. She might laugh at Violet and think I was babyish. I thought about that and left my old rag doll on the ragpile.

At quarter past three it was time for Mammy and me to leave as well. There'd been no suitcase to pack, no sorting out of a few precious objects that might make me feel more at home in my new surroundings. No one thought to suggest that I nip down the road and say goodbye to Little Tommy and his wife, or pay a quick visit to Mr and Mrs Sheard on Water's Road. I simply buttoned up my blue gabardine and Mammy threw on an old fawn mackintosh that she'd hacked the hem off, and we were ready to leave.

At the bus stop Mammy poked through her purse for the right amount of fare whilst I stood quietly, saying my own farewells to the grey moors, the grey shapes of boulders and the great, grey sky.

As the little red bus rumbled down the road I watched everything familiar flash past me. Dots of sheep slipped by like clouds in wind. Up came Boat Lane where hawthorn hips mixed into winter branches, like cherries in Christmas cake, then were gone. Soon the little mill town of Marsden was behind me and Slaithwaite, as alien to me as Halifax, loomed ahead. The landscape was similar to the one I had left behind, but more green and fertile. Some of it I remembered passing the day I had gone in search of Mammy when Nanna was badly: a little bungalow here, a mill there.

"H'ours is t' next stop," said Mammy as we passed a sunken graveyard on our left and a long row of narrow terraces with tarmac yards. The conductor pinged the bell and as we rose up from our seats, Mammy pointed to the Drill Hall. "It's where 'Wainwright' used to practice marching up and down when he was in the territorials," she remarked.

We walked down a short but sharp incline that led us past another row of dingy terraced houses and into the village. Mammy pointed to the Winston Cinema.

"That's where ah used to watch silent movies when ah was a girl. A woman used t' sit at front n' play t'pianer. An' wen we came h'out we used t'buy a penny worth er chips from Meal's, t'fish shop on Britannia Road."

Mammy rattled off memory after fond memory of Slaithwaite. I did not share her view.

There was a coldness and a clamminess in the air as we made our way along almost deserted streets. On both sides of the road, shops were full of Christmas decorations. In one window, a large sign saying 'Order Your Christmas Cakes Here.' had an iced cake placed temptingly underneath it. A ruff of green paper frilled around its rim, and on top stood a jolly snowman and a little cottage covered with a canopy of snow. But all the tinsel was like snakes, and the decorations chains, conspiring together to keep me trapped in Slaithwaite. Mammy didn't seem to notice, and kept chuntering on about places she knew.

"That's t'Globe Worsted Mill," she chattered, "Ah once worked there as a Feeder, years ago... n' just h'over there," she pointed a bony finger towards another road that was flanked by a long row of shops and a wide pavement, "h'is Crimble. That's where me n' Wainwright lived wen we first got married... But we're not goin' on there, we're goin' this way - up t'station steps."

A little grocer's shop called Wallaces was advertising Robinson's Mincemeat and Rowntrees Sunripe Jelly. On our right was a tall stone War Memorial splashed with poppies, the only thing to penetrate the grey. Our journey seemed endless. After climbing a steep flight of steps close to a railway embankment, and a wide footpath covered in stone setts, Mammy led us to Hill Top. Hill Top was even worse than I'd imagined, just a long boring street with terraced houses on both sides. Only by looking over the rooftops and gazing far into the distance could you see anything that resembled grassland. There were no hills to climb, no little streams to jump across and no wild flowers to pick, only a few straggly strands of groundsel growing in the gutter. Even they looked drab and depressed.

Mammy was taking me to Union Street, a little farther on, up a narrow cobbled road that separated one miserable back yard after another. It was Whitely Street all over again; out-houses, stone coal 'oles, bare yards. After the wide-open space of Marsden moor, Union Street was a quarry too steep to climb out of.

Auntie Alice's was about a third of the way up. A black Austin A35 was parked outside on the cobbles.

"This looks like it," said Mammy, leading me towards a dark green door that had a black number six nailed to it. Net curtains hung crisp and toothpaste-white across sparkling windows. Peeping through the lacy holes was a light so bright it made me shrink back.

Union Street

"Cum on," urged Mammy. She began mounting two or three stone steps that led to a little wooden gate and from there into a tarmac yard no bigger than a handkerchief. I dragged behind.

"Looks like h'Alice 'as been scourin' t'steps," she said, nodding to a thin yellow line that ran round the top step of a further flight of four. It looked like donkey stone, the stuff Nanna had had on a shelf under the stairs - a relic of the days before Kathleen died.

What was Mammy thinking as she knocked on the door? Was she glad to be ridding herself of the mucky little urchin beside her? Or was she a little sad at loosing her only remaining daughter? Maybe she felt nothing – she certainly didn't show any emotion, and neither did I.

Mammy knocked again. This time, Alice, smartly dressed in a pleated skirt and Bri-nylon cardigan, opened the door. A faint smell of flowery scent opened out with her. I had a good look at Alice, she was firm and shapely. I had often seen advertisements in the Colne Valley Guardian for pink corsets and steys. I decided that must be what she was wearing under her over-garments. Then remembering it was rude to stare, my gaze fell floorward.

"Come in, come in." She stepped aside, ushering us into a long-by-narrow kitchen. I was overwhelmed by warmth and clean and baking. "Pass me your coats and I'll hang them in the hall."

For a brief moment we were left alone. I looked around and noticed that the ceiling was horribly high, and that the floor was covered in patterned linoleum. A white pot sink stood against one wall and next to that an electric cooker. On a shelf above, a set of saucepans glinted in the bright light. To my right was a tiny window with cherry red curtains and a small potted plant absorbing what little light it could from the dull December day. In the background I could hear Auntie Alice shouting, "Elizabeth! Heather's here, come and say hello." Within seconds a tubby little girl emerged from another room. She was all dressed up in her Sunday best - a gold Lurex frock with a frilly net petticoat beneath it. Her chestnut hair, tied back in a neat ponytail, was fastened at the top in a golden bow. My own hair had not been washed since the day Mammy had abducted me from The Home. I hung my head lower than my matted rats' tails. Then I saw my own frock, which might have been white and posh twenty years ago but now the silk and satin were grimed with tea stains and old coal dust. I hung my head even lower.

This house was too clean to cope with. Elizabeth stared, her eyes blue as Forget-me-nots, her complexion flawless. She reminded me of 'Princess Anne – Bridesmaid'.

Standing behind Elizabeth was her older brother Edward and his girlfriend, Daphne. Edward was twenty-one and unlike my older brother Graham, who was thin and dark, Edward was fair and stocky.

"So you're Heather? Smiled Edward. "And you must be Kitty? Nice to see you." He shook Mammy's hand. "We've just decorated the tree, why don't you come through and have a look? I'm sure you'll like it."

He led us in to the front room where the tall Christmas tree gleamed in the corner. The baubles reflected in his shoes, and in each of these baubles, a tiny, perfect

Edward shone back. The entire tree became a mirrorball of Edwards in tweed ties and pressed trousers, joined by immaculate Daphnes. I thought of Graham at home in his frayed shirt and greasy overalls, and could look at the tree no longer.

Uncle Edgar was sitting in an armchair smoking his pipe, the smell reminded me of woodsmoke. A pair of horn rimmed glasses, not unlike the ones Nanna used to wear, rested upon his nose.

"Come and sit by the fire," he said, "and get warm."

The heat on my legs, as I drew near, felt too much, like the rest of the house. Elizabeth, plonked on the furry hearthrug, her eyes not leaving us once. After a while she jumped up and asked me if I would like to look at her black doll.

"Auntie Lucy bought it for my birthday," she chirped.

Somehow I managed to mumble yes.

"There's no need to be shy." Uncle Edgar noted my reticence amongst swirls of blue smoke. "This is your home now."

But my home was out on the moors where the sun slanted through the little windows and candlelight flickered across the dingy walls on dark evening. Homesickness burst in upon me, and my throat became tight and sore like it had in the 'Homes' when Auntie Flossy or Jean were shouting or teasing, and sometimes still did when I thought of Nanna. But I knew that to cry would only cause everyone to look at me and I couldn't stand the fuss. I had to gulp it back, and focus instead on Elizabeth's celluloid doll (which was as well dressed as its owner in a pale lavender frock and lilac cardigan) Auntie Alice stuck her head round the door.

"Tea's ready, if you would like to come through."

She ushered us into the dining room to a table laid with a white linen cloth, as sprucely set as everything else I'd seen. In the centre of the table stood a small glass milk jug and a sugar basin. By each place setting, which was made up of a silver knife and fork and a dessert spoon, sat a cup, a saucer and a small plate. Although the cups, saucers and side plates were the same pattern, each place setting was of a different colour. Auntie Alice led me to the blue set and Mammy to the maroon. Mammy sat stiffly on the chair opposite, gazing at her tea plate. I felt so sorry for her. Why couldn't we just catch the next bus home?

The polished room and exquisite table looked back at me through an oval mirror in a guilded frame above the fireplace. Beneath the mirror, orderly china ornaments sat on the gleaming mantelshelf. The most suprising thing of all was a budgerigar cooped up in a cage in a corner by the window.

"That's Sugar our budgie," said Elizabeth proudly, poking her finger through the bar and making the little bird flap around screeching "Sugar's a bugger, Sugar's a bugger."

"Help yourselves to some salad." Auntie Alice pointed her silver fork to a large bowl stuffed with lettuce and tomatoes. "And there's plenty of boiled ham too, so don't be afraid to fill your plates."

I poked around, finally stabbing a bit of ham which flopped back onto its plate. I eventually rescued it after a struggle, and set it down next to a wedge of tomato. It would have been so much easier to use my fingers.

Elizabeth, snug between Edward and Daphne, was already scooping up sliced egg, pork pie and pieces of cucumber, and putting the lot onto her plate.

"Here, try some of this." Auntie Alice scooped a large spoon full of fresh lettuce onto my plate. Then balancing a slice of boiled ham onto a bone handled knife placed it carefully in front of Mammy.

"Er... ah don't want any er them tomatoes... thank you," muttered Mammy. Her eyes were fixed firmly on the large silver spoon that Auntie Alice was about to dip in the tomato bowl. "Ah've 'eard that them there seed's at's in em can give yer cancer."

Auntie Alice almost dropped the silver server into her teacup, and glancing to see if Elizabeth had heard, said, "Not they, Kitty. Who ever told yer that?"

Mammy gave a nervous giggle. "T'doctor once told mi mother."

"So what's your favourite subject at school then, Heather?" Asked Edward, trying to change the subject, and, as an added distraction began pouring himself a cup of tea.

"Comperzisherns." I whispered.

"Mine's sewing," interjected Elizabeth. "I like embroidery. I'll show you a tray cloth I'm making for my mum after tea. I'm going to knit myself a sweater too. I've already got the wool, its green with red flecks in."

"Elizabeth goes ballroom dancing as well," said Daphne, lifting up her empty cup and passing it to Edward. "Perhaps you could go too."

I thought of spangly dresses and shuddered. I wanted to say "Well actually I like playing out best, n' one day I'm going to have a norse er me own so I won't 'ave much time fer stuff like that." Instead I smiled timidly and continued to push the cold meat around my china plate.

There was an immense trifle, topped with double cream and grated chocolate for dessert. Daphne served it from a large glass bowl into delicate little dishes with thin stems. Auntie Alice disappeared into the kitchen and returned with a silver cake stand full of homemade buns and ribbon cake.

Apart from Mammy's bold statement about Cancer, she and I had scarcely said a word throughout. Although everyone had tried to include us in the conversation, our answers were limited to a couple of words. The budgie had more to say than us, as it hopped from one end of its perch to the other, crying "Who's a little sweetheart," and pecking its mirror.

"We'll leave the washing up till later." Auntie Alice pushed back her chair and straightened her skirt. "I know Edward will want to get off."

Edward, she continued, was a conscript in the army, based at some far off place called Basingstoke. The Austin outside was his and he was due back at base that very evening and had no time to waste. He and Daphne were due to get married on New Years Eve, Elizabeth was to be a bridesmaid.

I was in the other room when mammy left. She'd seemed to disappear around the same time as Daphne and Edward. I'd been trying to guess Elizabeth's middle name, and hadn't realised she'd gone for some time. She hadn't come through to say goodbye, but instead sneaked off so as not to upset me.

After casually telling me that Mammy had gone, Auntie Alice scuttled off into the other room and I could hear the clink of china as she began clearing the table. Elizabeth nudged me, "Guess again, guess again." After a few lame guesses, I muttered 'Violet'.

"You'll never get it," grinned Elizabeth, "It's Marguerite." She was right, I'd never have got it.

Uncle Edgar remained slouched in the easy chair puffing on his pipe. Not only did he work all day in a factory, Elizabeth told me, but by evening he was a steward at a local Working Men's Club.

"What would you like for Christmas?" asked Elizabeth, busily dressing and undressing her 'Rosebud' doll. "I want Toy Balloons." I must have looked a bit blank because she went on to explain "It's a record by Russ Conway – you know, he plays the piano."

She darted over to a large radiogram and lifted the lid. She was just about to demonstrate a record by this Russ Conway when Auntie Alice breezed in.

"Come on you two, it's seven o'clock - bath time."

"Arghh…" grumbled Elizabeth, who was busy sorting through a large selection of thin black discs in jazzy envelopes, which were much smaller than Graham's old 78's and twice as shiny. "Just let me play this for Heather, she's *never even heard of Russ Conway!*"

"Just two minutes then. And no longer!"

It only took a matter of seconds for Elizabeth to whip the record out of its sleeve and place it on the turntable. With a quick flick of her wrist she pressed something-or-other inside the cabinet and the arm containing the needle swung into action. Amazing! There was no handle to crank, no crackling sounds to distort the music and the record never got stuck. Nor did it grind to a halt. The music just kept on playing.

Still humming the notes of her favourite 'pop tune', Elizabeth fairly danced up the stairsteps. I trudged behind her, each thick, carpeted step wearier than the last. The bathroom was nice though: a far cry from our grotty slop bucket and spidery lavatory. It had a large white bathtub with chrome taps, a washbasin which had Armitage Shanks written in blue letters above the plughole - and a toilet - all in the same room!

"It's school in the morning," said Auntie Alice, briskly. "So we must get you looking all nice and clean." She drew some water from the hot tap and I watched nervously as it spurted into the deep bath. Auntie Alice then carefully removed the wrapping from a silver cube and passed it to Elizabeth. Elizabeth dropped it into the water with a loud plop. Suddenly a strong smell of roses was all about us. By now Elizabeth was stripped off and ready to climb in. I hung about like a shy kitten.

"You can have a bath when Elizabeth gets out," said Auntie Alice. She began folding her daughter's clothes and placing them neatly on to the lid of a linen basket. I wondered if I was the last to wash because Alice didn't want Elizabeth to 'catch owt'. After a lot of splashing about and swilling of hair, Elizabeth climbed out.

"Your turn now." Auntie Alice looked at me. I stood still, hot and embarrassed under the red glowing heater on the ceiling. "Chop, chop,"

Slowly I got undressed. In the shiny green tiles I saw myself, a newborn bird with bits of bones sticking out all over the place, at the side of the plump, pink-skinned Elizabeth.

After pouring a thimble full of brown medicated Loxene onto the palm of her hand Auntie Alice began washing my hair with the tips of her fingers, scraping my scalp. The carbolicy smell reminded me of The Cottage Homes. After swilling away the soapsuds, Auntie Alice picked up a double-sided nailbrush and scrubbed the muck off my arms and legs like rust off an old bike.

"You could grow potatoes in here," she said, screwing the corner of the flannel into a tight knot, and digging into my ears. Elizabeth laughed. Auntie Alice handed me one of the blue and white striped towels which had been hanging neat on the chrome rail, then turned her attention to a pink plastic cup full of toothbrushes and paste.

Twenty minutes later Elizabeth and I were downstairs smelling of Pears soap and 'French Moss' talcum powder. Auntie Alice found me a blue flannelette nightdress to put on.

"Next week, when Miss Newton comes," she said, "We'll see about getting you some new clothes. In the mean time you can wear some of Elizabeth's."

I had never worn a nightdress before, not even in the Home, and I didn't like it. I would have given anything to go to bed in my dirty old dress and mucky socks, like I did at home.

The long day wasn't over until we'd had supper, a glass of cold milk and a slice of bread and butter which Auntie Alice had smeared homemade lemon cheese on to. I found it almost impossible to swallow.

"Say goodnight to Uncle Edgar, Heather," said Auntie Alice, finally.

Goodnight was not a word I used and it came out as a useless squeak. Elizabeth, on the other hand, danced across the room and planted a big kiss on her father's cheek. I hurried to the door just in case they expected me to do the same.

"Up them 'apple's and pear's." Uncle Edgar joked.

"Come on, race you upstairs, Heather," grinned Elizabeth.

All I wanted to do was race home.

"This is your room." Elizabeth flung open a door at the far end of the landing. It was as spick and span as the rest of the house, and as full of squeaky newness, from the sickly pink vase on the chest of drawers, to the faint smell of paint. A picture of Elizabeth in a wool dress and cardigan grinned goofily at me. The real Elizabeth, scampered across the landing to her own room, and I slunk into bed. Auntie Alice bounded in a moment later to tuck me in. I shrank away from her kiss, and covered myself with the pink eiderdown. "See you in the morning, Heather," she said. "If there's anything you want just give me a shout."

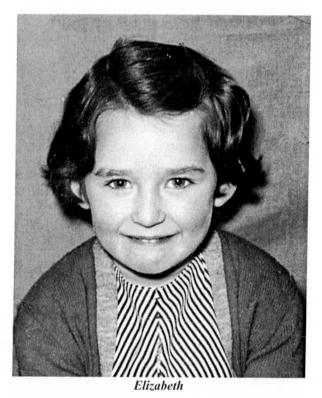

Elizabeth

It hadn't been long since Mrs Reed had said the same thing when I was cosy in her big pyjamas under Rupert's quilt. Now, I was in bed without a book or my ball for company.

Don't Cry Nanna

The stiff sheets and starched pillow slips at Auntie Alice's felt too crisp and clean and I remembered how, not too long ago, I had curled up on the flock tickin with Nanna. I was glad that Mammy had snatched me from The Home before Nanna died. But now, all that was over and somehow I couldn't see myself conforming to a life of knit one purl one and dancing lessons. I was like a baby cuckoo in the wrong nest. Nothing seemed real here, even the single stemmed roses on the wallpaper stared back false and stiff. The reality lived in my mind, where red velvet roses tumbled over a wall near Blakelea, and Mr Sheard bent over to pick one of his delicate pink blooms and share its scent with me.

I could climb onto my stone aeroplane right now, if I wanted to, and fly over the place where Pink Purslane grew free.

AFTERWORD

The story doesn't quite end there. How could it, when we all had the rest of our lives to get on with. The life of Millstone Cottages, however, was doomed shortly after when the last tenants moved out and the buildings were bulldozed. They'd been condemned for long enough. I never managed to get to that funeral either, to pay last respects to the settling dust.

Graham refused to leave the place he called home and spent most of the year in a caravan on the edge of the moor. But waking up on cold November mornings with a covering of frost on the blankets and sometimes condensation dripping from the ceiling like a leaking tap, almost gave him pneumonia. After a serious bout of flu during his third season, Graham had to give up his gypsy lifestyle and move in with Mammy in Marsden full time. He eventually rented a mill house on Brougham Road, and five years later in 1974 married Muriel. He retired from the mill after forty years of faithful service.

They still live happily in the same house and I always enjoy popping in, for Graham and Muriel always have a tale to tell, and in winter a fire roars up the chimney.

As for Arnold, he remained at Dryfield House till he was old enough to become independent. They had taken him aside quietly after school to tell him about Nanna. He had been brave and not cried, just uttered 'oh'. We eventually discovered, to our mutual surprise that Dryfield House was only a ten-minute walk away from The Cottage Homes! Arnold left a young man, and went back into the world to live with Alice's sister Esther and ended up with Mammy in Marsden. He met, and married Ann, and moved to Linthwaite till after his daughter was born in 1970. The family flitted back to Mammy's while Arnold went over to find lodgings and work in North Wales. By 1972, the Wainwrights moved into a tiny bungalow they'd bought in Kinmel Bay, just outside Rhyl. Arnold had a job with Ann's brother's Tarmac Contracting Company and a year later, Arnold's son was born. (The name John Strong hadn't quite deserted him for he had Johnny Starr[*] tattooed on his arm, and christened his own son John.)

When they grew up, his daughter Jill and her family settled back in Marsden, and John moved to Sheffield. Arnold also moved back, alone, changed his name

---

[*] *Arnold was the tambourine player in a band called 'Johnny Starr & The Units' when he was a teenager. They had cards printed up, advertising their 'Beat Music at its Best'. Graham still has the tambourine.*

to Jon, and currently lives in Slaithwaite.

And whatever became of Mammy? Well, she finally left that Goblin Topczewski, who died anyway not long after, and spent the rest of her life in Marsden. First, at Argyle Street, after they pulled down the houses which backed onto the river, opening up the view, then later a council bungalow up Woods Avenue, and finally one of the old peoples council flats on Carrs Road. She stopped drinking, but carried on her strange ways. Graham was always finding cast-off furniture in the garden, smashed to smithereens, the toilet cistern stuffed with rags so it wouldn't flush or the gas fire pulled apart. She ate that much sugary food that it gave her the energy to shift all her furniture around (she would frequently load her TV onto a chair and wheel it to its new location.)

To her grandchildren, she became batty grandma – a cute little woman with 'funny' ways, but a heart of gold. She treated them all equally, and never bought for one without buying for the rest.

She died in 1995 just before her 85th birthday, having lived a long, fairly healthy lifetime of bizarre behaviour. She ended up with two Great grandchildren whose names she could never remember so she called them 'That Little Boy' and 'It'.

Of the other people I mention, who lived in and around the village, some are still alive and well like Mr and Mrs Iredale and David. Nellie Beardsall finally shut up shop as recently as 1999, after 80 years of service. Mr and Mrs Sheard became a distant memory and sadly I never heard from the Reeds again, though I did hear that they'd moved away.

As for me, my story could have continued if I'd have wanted it to. Shortly after moving into my Auntie's, I was given a book called 'Jill's Gymkhana', which I still have. The main character was a little girl from a not-too-well-off family, who strove for a pony of her own. Her dream came true, and so did mine eventually.

We moved from Union Street up to the Rose and Crown pub at Cop Hill in Slaithwaite, a much more remote place, almost like the wilds of Standedge – but not quite. Gradually, I got used to living with my Auntie Alice and Uncle Edgar, and found them firm but kind. And before long, decided that I would never want to go without the comforts of a clean bed and a spotless hankie.

I bought my first horse in 1965 at the age of 16 - a dark bay Anglo-Arab called Midnight, or Cussop First Choice if we were being really posh. Along with my best friend, Maz, who was also horse mad, and owned a beautiful 15.2hh chestnut gelding called Joker, I competed at many local shows. We enjoyed long rides across the moor and talked non-stop about equestrian matters.

Elizabeth, although not 'horsy', became a friend/sister (we never knew what to introduce ourselves as.) She was, and still is, more interested in dressing up in smart clothes and shoes than tramping across a field in a pair of muddy wellies.

One thing which shocked me as I grew up was discovering that my name wasn't Heather at all, but Muriel (my father probably registered me, naming me after his sister, and my mother had rebelled.)

I married Robert in 1969 and we lived in a very basic cottage at Cop Hill with our two children Michelle and Matthew, and various pets, until moving into our dream cottage (just like Jill's, in Jill's Gymkhana) further down the road nearer Slaithwaite, which we renovated ourselves. Robert and I still live there today with Nell our border collie, Martha the cat (and Jacob, stabled just down the road.)

I haven't mentioned Wainwright yet. I hardly ever saw my father after he took my mother and me to The Junction in Longroyd Bridge. I noticed him in the market hall once, when I was with my friend Maz, and avoided any embarrassment to either of us by not approaching him. I often wish I'd have sought him out and looked after him before he died (over twenty years ago.) Today, I have a good relationship with Wainwright's sister Muriel, who has told me stories of the brother she knew as Charlie (before my mother started referring to him as Wainwright, she called him 'Chorles'.)

What I've found most ironic is that both my daughter Michelle and I are residential social workers, Michelle even works in a children's home on the site where the Cottage Homes used to be.

Yes, they were eventually pulled down, but Beech Towers remained a hospital.

I'm a Nanna now, with three wonderful grandchildren who all live nearby. They help in my garden, and love coming to jumble sales in Marsden with me. They also enjoy sharing my almost complete collection of Rupert annuals, Rupert never deserted me as a child, and now I'm not deserting him.

As a final point of interest, I recently spent an evening at Graham's when he produced a well preserved little green book. It was his 1956 Filmgoers Diary. Scrawled between the pages of Sunday the ninth and Tuesday the eleventh of September were the following lines Nanna had recited and I had copied.

> *"Think of me when thou art lonely,*
> *Keep for me one silent spot*
> *In the depths of your affections*
> *Plant me one Forget-me-not.*
> *When the burning sun is setting*
> *And your thoughts of care are free,*
> *Whilst of others you are thinking*
> *Will you sometimes think of me."*